Th
IRONSTONE
of the
MIDLANDS

History, Operation and Railways

Part IV

The Wellingborough Area

by

Eric Tonks

M.Sc., F.R.I.C., Dip.Maths

Book Law Publications
Nottingham

© Eric Tonks 1990

ISBN 978-1-907094-03-3

First Published in 1990
by
Runpast Publishing

This Edition Published in 2009
by
Book Law Publications

Printed by The Amadeus Press, Cleckheaton, BD19 4TQ

Irchester Quarries. HOLWELL NO.30 eases a loaded train round the curve to the BR sidings on 3rd August 1967. View taken from the bridge under Rushden Road.   M.J. Leah

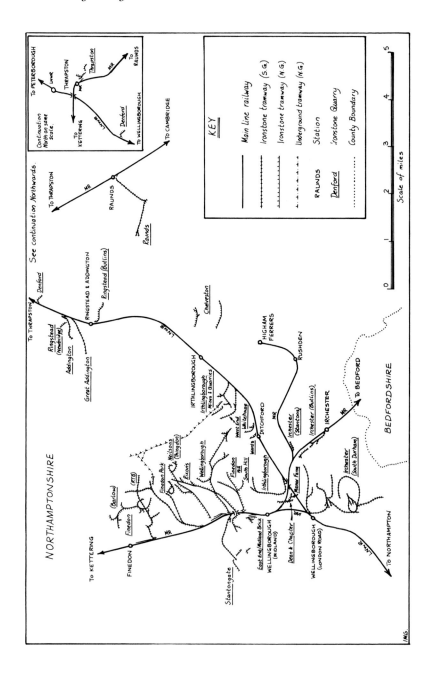

CONTENTS

ACKNOWLEDGEMENTS

I have had to rely heavily on the help of local people, as acknowledged (fully, I hope) in the text. In addition I should mention John Bailey and Ted Amey, who as local historians of Finedon put me in touch with old employees with worthwhile information and interesting photographs. Also I must as always thank those personal friends who have helped from their specialist knowledge and skills. Ian Lloyd for his excellent maps, painstakingly redrawn when I have made errors: Norman Bellamy and Alan Pack (surveyors) for material from BSC archives: Geoffrey Starmer, for his knowledge of Northamptonshire archaeology and his fine photograph collection: Greg Evans for information and photographs from old employees: Marshall Fayers for his knowledge of quarry machines: Geoffrey Webb for his meticulous records of main line railways: and Martin Davies for his critical review of the text and for copying archival photographs. This brief acknowledgement bears no relation to the extent of the help they have freely given me over many years; without them and the photographers who have kindly allowed me to use their work, this book would not have been possible.

INTRODUCTION

The Wellingborough Area

The main subject of this Part is the complex of workings within a three-mile radius to the east of Wellingborough, from Finedon in the north through Irthlingborough (E.N.E.) to Irchester (W.S.W.). Within this area almost the entire ground above the 300-foot contour has been exploited for ironstone either by quarrying or mining. Also included are a few outlying quarries further up the Nene valley as far as Thrapston, most of which had associations with Wellingborough operators.

Development was contemporaneous with the Northampton area, but was influenced, particularly in the 19th century, to a much greater extent by the local ironworks, and as a result only a small proportion of the ore was sent away. Of the thirty quarries described, fifteen were opened in the period 1852–75, all but four in 1873–75 directly controlled by the owners of the furnaces at Wellingborough, Irthlingborough and Finedon. The 1870's was the period of greatest expansion, with eleven quarries opened, with operators outside Wellingborough taking an interest; chief among them was Stanton Ironworks Co Ltd, who played an increasingly important part in the development of Wellingborough ironworks.

From the railway viewpoint matters were simple, as only three lines were involved – the LNWR Blisworth–Peterborough line, the MR main line through Wellingborough (opened 1857) and the MR Kettering–Cambridge line that served two quarries in the north-east corner of the district. The LNWR line, as the earliest, was the one that fostered the initial development, and eventually served about half the quarries described. The ironworks all had internal tramway systems that conveyed the ore direct from quarry to furnace without using the main line railways; from the start Butlins also supplied ironworks elsewhere, as in the last stage so did Wellingborough ironworks. The tramways comprised the usual mixture of narrow and standard gauges, the characteristics of which are dealt with in the text; and there were some oddities, as at Stanton's Irchester quarries, where the ore seems to have been shovelled directly into wagons from the railway cutting; at Chelveston, with a mixture of narrow gauge tramway and road carts; and Butlin's short-lived tramway to the river Nene, about which almost nothing is known.

Wellingborough is an 'old' area, and nearly all the sites were opened before 1900. Of the seven that came later, three were prompted by World War I (Ditchford (Wards): Finedon Park: Irthlingborough mines) and of these only the last was of importance; and four that were revivals of older workings (Denford: Finedon: South Hill Farm: Midland Brick). The last surviving ironworks, at Wellingborough, was closed during the Depression but was completely rebuilt on modern lines, the quarry tramway also, so that it was virtually a new system. From the outbreak of World War II only five quarries were in production – Finedon: Midland Brick: Irthlingborough: Wellingborough: Irchester. The last two, with lives of 92 and 94 years respectively, were the longest-lived systems in the district. These all had special features of interest – Irchester with its 'Colonel Stephens' approach to locomotive usage and its numerous steam quarry machines; Wellingborough with its modernised metre gauge tramway and complex mining history; Finedon with its heavy engineering features; Irthlingborough with its mining system, by then extended through to Finedon; and Midland Brick, which was the first known ironstone quarry to use lorries.

One of the principal features of this district was the emphasis on mining, which reached its most successful development at Irthlingborough and Wellingborough, following earlier experiments at Thingdon and Finedon Hill. On the surface, quarry machines were only employed at four quarries – Irchester, Wellingborough, Finedon and Midland Brick; the last had only one machine, in 1940, but the other three had large and interesting fleets.

Without doubt, the history of the workings in the Wellingborough area have proved one of the most difficult to unravel, because of the imperfect documentation for the early years and, later on, by the intensive working by several operators in close proximity. The difficulties are not confined to very early days, though; elucidation of the succession of changes in the tramways at Thingdon/Wellingborough mines in the 1920's and 1930's proved a real headache; and it was not until 1986 that the separate identity of the South Hill Farm system was pieced together. Further afield, I had to wait until 1987 to pinpoint Newbridge Iron Ore Co's Ringstead quarries.

Fortunately for the industrial archaeologists, two of the sites have been saved by local authorities. Irchester Country Park is on unrestored quarrying land bearing many traces of former activity and here also are ironstone locomotives restored by the Irchester Narrow Gauge Railway

Trust; while at Finedon the railway cuttings have been made into an attractive nature trail. Elsewhere near Wellingborough there are bits and pieces that are likely to remain for a good many years yet, and I hope that the text will enable explorers to place these in their historical context. At Irthlingborough there has been much building in recent years, but some traces can be seen, and the quarries further up the Nene valley, though small and not of much consequence, were set in more attractive countryside.

Irchester was the place I visited most in working days, walking up Newtown Road in Little Irchester and taking the public footpath that so conveniently crossed the mineral line a few yards below the engine shed; then up the line past the calcine banks to the workshops, where there was an ever-changing array of partly dismantled locomotives for examination, plus the working ones coming up from the pits. Wellingborough quarries offered less variety in locomotives but had the special charm inseparable from the narrow gauge; and there was always the flagman on Ryebury Hill crossing. In more recent years I have made numerous visits in attempts to elucidate the past. The sombre pines clothing the slopes of No. 1 Quarry at Wellingborough stir the imagination to recall the days of mining here; while at the other end of the district is Raunds with its remote station and almost complete lack of any traces in this flat land.

Birmingham, 1990   Eric Tonks

Readers' attention is drawn to the explanation of abbreviations in the text and terms used in tables of locomotives and equipment, listed on pages 222–225

The maps have all been prepared by Ian Lloyd.

KEY TO INDIVIDUAL QUARRY MAPS

————————	Main line railway
FINEDON	Station
+·+·+·+·+·+·+·+	Ironstone tramway (standard gauge)
·———·———·———·	Ironstone tramway (narrow gauge)
═·═·═·═·═·═	Ironstone tramway (rope worked incline)
⌐└─	Roads
Irchester	Village
Finedon Quarries	Ironstone Quarry
⌐‾‾‾˜˜‾⌐	Area of Quarry working
Lodge	Quarry face
↙ 1939 / 1942	Direction of Quarrying and dates of operation.

THE WELLINGBOROUGH GROUP

The history of the Wellingborough area has proved the most difficult of all to unravel. This was particularly the case for the early years; official statistics of the 1850's are lacking or incomplete, and many small quarries were opened and closed before being recorded on the 1883/4 OS maps. Some leases for the period 1850–80 have been preserved but it has not been possible in some cases to identify the sites, including some that survived long enough to be shown on the OS.

The first quarry (Manor Farm) was opened in 1852, with connection to the LNWR Blisworth–Peterborough line, by S.H. Blackwell, who was closely involved in the developments arising from the specimens of ore shown at the Great Exhibition of 1851; but his efforts were immediately eclipsed by the activities of Thomas Butlin, whose ironworks at East End, Wellingborough, started production in 1853. At that time Wellingborough consisted of a small group of houses with a path to All Hallows church on the hilltop to the north; the ironworks lay to the east, surrounded by small ironstone quarries operated by horse-worked tramways – but there was no connection to the main line railway. This factor hampered development so much that Butlin built his Irthlingborough ironworks just outside the town, with the convenience of railway access, commencing production in 1867; the old works was 'phased out' and the area round it engulfed in the rapid expansion of Wellingborough in late Victorian times. The new ironworks was in Irthlingborough parish, as it lay on the east bank of the river Ise (hereabouts the parish boundary between Wellingborough and Irthlingborough) but geographically it was very close to the new town of Wellingborough, and is often referred to in early records, official correspondence and everyday conversation as 'Wellingborough Ironworks', which has led to further confusion. In the account that follows, therefore, we can only give such data as have been preserved or established, and leave some queries for local historians to unravel.

WELLINGBOROUGH EAST END IRONWORKS QUARRIES

Owners: Thomas Butlin & Co;
Butlin Bevan & Co from 17th December 1861

The East End Works was the first ironworks to be built actually in the Northamptonshire ironstone field; the exhibition of samples of ore from the county at the Great Exhibition of 1851 encouraged Thomas Butlin to erect an experimental furnace at Northampton and afterwards – following the discovery of substantial beds of ironstone in the neighbourhood of Wellingborough and Higham Ferrers – to build his East End Works under the style of Thomas Butlin & Co. The first furnace was put in blast in June 1853[1] and was fed with ore garnered from the immediate vicinity, testified by the sunken areas in the neighbourhood of Finedon Road, and now occupied by parks and allotments; on the north side west of Cross Road, and on the south side west of Eastfield Road (which did not then exist) and also on the north side of Nest Lane.

The first mention in MS of quarries in connection with East End Works is 1858, and the source of ore before that time is uncertain, though it seems safe to assume that it was dug on the ground belonging to the ironworks (or to William Butlin) and not brought in from outside. According to Hewlett, ironstone and other materials were brought to the works in carts; the ground lay north and east of the old town of Wellingborough, and much of the area was built over in Victorian times. On 26th November 1859 the company leased six fields from Henry B. Whitworth for a period of fourteen years from Michaelmas 1859, and renewable for a further fourteen years if required. The ground comprised 56 acres and had been a 'larger area before part was used for the railway'. It included ground between Mill Road and Finedon Road on the west side of, and immediately adjacent to, the Midland Railway, which area Hewlett notes as having been worked by Butlins; confirmation is provided by the names of the six fields quoted in the lease and which can be identified by means of the Map and Key in Joyce & Maurice Palmer's '*A History of Wellingborough*' (Steeple Press, Earls Barton, 1972).

The ironstone workings were taken over by a partnership formed on 16th December 1861 of William Butlin, Edwin Butlin, George Edward Bevan and Alfred Elton under the name Butlin, Bevan & Co, who took over the unexpired part of the above lease on the following day. The partnership agreement stated that the original proprietors had 'latterly opened pits on part of the said land, laying down tramway sidings and other works for conveying away the ironstone'; a process that they doubtless continued. Another parcel of land, twelve acres in extent, was leased from the Church Commissioners on 25th March 1862, and was described as the Church Headland Close in the East Field; the lessees are given as Thos Butlin & Co and not Butlin, Bevan & Co. The site was a couple of fields south of Finedon Road, immediately east of what became Eastfield Road, i.e. west of Midland Brickworks. Similarly, there were 'several pieces of land in Wellingborough' leased for 21 years from Mary Ann Elizabeth Gibbs, about which nothing further is known. Some of Butlin's workings (possibly those covered by the Gibbs lease) were later connected by tramway to the standard gauge line serving Stantongate quarries, owned by Stanton Ironworks Co Ltd – which see.

Full details of the tramways are not known, and only two are shown on the earliest available OS map (1883) which was well after East End Works had closed down. The area between Cannon Street and the Midland Railway was served by a standard gauge tramway with two principal branches – each with two passing loops – that converged at a point later occupied by the Midland Brickworks, and then joined, via a reversing point, a Midland Railway siding opposite the locomotive shed yard. It is presumed that these were operated by horses, but locomotives are not ruled out; on the other hand, gravity working may have been used, with horses to pull the wagons back. The last entry in MS under the heading 'East End Works' is dated 1874, suggesting that the 14-year lease was not renewed (unless perhaps for one year); it is however possible that Butlin, Bevan carried on, the output covered by the general entry 'Wellingborough Quarries'. The area east of Eastfield Road was later developed by Midland Brick Co (Wellingborough) Ltd – which see – but west of the road was almost wholly built upon.

The other tramway was probably a narrow gauge line operated by horse, running to a roadside tipping stage, and is referred to in 1885[2] when an ironstone labourer was killed by being run over by a loaded wagon; this was "at the tip on the road leading from Gold Street, belonging to Messrs Butlin's iron pits". There may well have been other short tramways of similar type in this area, lifted before the OS was made.

East End Works was vacated by Butlins in 1875 and operated for a year by Lyttle's Iron Agency, closing about April 1876.[3]

Footnotes

1. Letter from 'R.V.' written 16th May 1853 in *Mining Journal* 21st May 1853; "At Wellingborough...the first furnace will be in blast in less than a month".
2. *Kettering Observer*, 21st August 1885.
3. *Kettering Guardian*, 30th April 1926 (in the column headed "50 years ago").

MANOR FARM QUARRIES

Owners: S.H. Blackwell and S.W. Smith

These quarries vie with Blackwell's workings at Hardingstone and Hickman's at Blisworth for pride of place as the first commercial ironstone quarries in Northamptonshire. On 13th February 1852 William Murphy of Wellingborough wrote to the occupier of Manor Farm, J.B. Howes, concerning the lease of ground for ironstone working; Howes had already agreed to lease some of his freehold land for £80 per year to Messrs Blackwell and Smith, and now the latter wished for a similar arrangement in respect of some land held by Howes on lease from the Dean & Chapter of Peterborough Cathedral, who were Lords of the Manor of Irthlingborough. Blackwell was an ironmaster of Dudley and Smith a financial colleague; Murphy was presumably a solicitor or agent acting on their behalf. Mr. Howes paid a visit to Peterborough and on his return called on Mr. Murphy with his findings; the Dean & Chapter were not agreeable to the proposal at that time because of the 'difficulty attending the granting of a lease for the minerals on the Irthlingborough Estate'. However, Blackwell and Smith evidently continued to work the land already leased, which comprised two fields on the east bank of the river Ise, on the north side of the public road to Irthlingborough, by Kilboon's Mill. It should be noted that this is called Mill Road, as is the road and bridleway a half mile to the north, that crosses the BR line north of Wellingborough station.

This ironstone outcrop site was later partly occupied by the Midland Railway main line, at that time not built. The Deposited Plans of the Midland Railway 'Leicester & Hitchin Railway', dated 28th November 1852, show the two fields leased to Blackwell and Smith and a 'tram road' ascribed to the same people, running in an arc across the field south of Mill Road to a point alongside the LNWR close to the bridge over the Nene. The fields on this side of the road were part of the Irthlingborough estate leased to Howes by the Cathedral, who must therefore have consented to a wayleave over the ground.

It is virtually certain that negotiations for the lease began in 1851, and that the quarry was in use late in that year or early in 1852; so this must indeed be the earliest ironstone tramway of which we have cartographical evidence. The quarry was not in use for very long, though; a letter dated 16th May 1853, signed 'R.V.' and published in *'Mining Journal'* of 21st

Manor Farm Quarries.   Possibly the earliest ironstone quarry in the Midlands, on the east bank of the river Ise, this was working in 1852, with a tramway connection to the LNWR – the MR main line then not being in existence. When the MR was built, it was necessary to put a bridge over the tramway. The quarry site was later occupied by part of Irthlingborough ironworks, and then by British Leyland's Nuffield Foundry, as here, 13th October 1985.

Eric Tonks

Manor Farm Quarries.   Blackwell's tramway crossed marshy ground to the LNWR – possibly by the shallow depression in the photo. The railway bridge over the Ise can be seen. In the 1860s the tramway was diverted to a wharf on the river. 24th December 1985.

Eric Tonks

May 1853, p.926, says '...in the deep cutting now being made in the quarries of Mr. Harris near Northampton and of Mr. Blackwell near Wellingborough...' and this is the last we know of it. No mention is made of it in MS, which publication had hardly had time to appreciate these new developments in ironstone; as an aside, it is interesting to note that the Deposited Plans refer to the workings as a 'stone pit', and that output from the 1859 quarry at Adderbury in Oxfordshire was consigned to the canal at 'Adderbury Stone Wharf' – the term 'ironstone quarry' had not by then become general.

Haulage over the line would presumably be by horse; of the gauge of the rails no record has survived – but see the discussion under the 'Dean & Chapter Quarries', under which guise the Manor Farm quarry was later reopened and worked. These are described separately because of significant differences; the presence of the MR line and the erection of Irthlingborough ironworks, both of which led to changes in the size of the quarries and, more particularly, the transport arrangements.

As this was probably the very first ironstone tramway, a visit to the site is worthwhile, though there is understandably little to be seen. The quarry area has completely disappeared under Irthlingborough ironworks (later B.L. Cars Ltd, Wellingborough Foundries) and the BR main line; but the bridge under the latter remains, and seems to have been enlarged and concreted as a route from the offices to the works. The point where the tramway crossed the Irthlingborough road is built up, but a public footpath by the side of the new premises of Alf Meade (Wellingborough) Ltd runs to a footbridge over the Nene close to the LNWR bridge, crossing the course of the former tramway route. A curving low embankment between shallow ditches could possibly indicate the trackbed, but this could be only a wishful thought. There are no traces at the LNWR end.

Grid References

908676	Quarry site
908675	Level crossing of Mill Road
912673	Tipping dock to LNWR

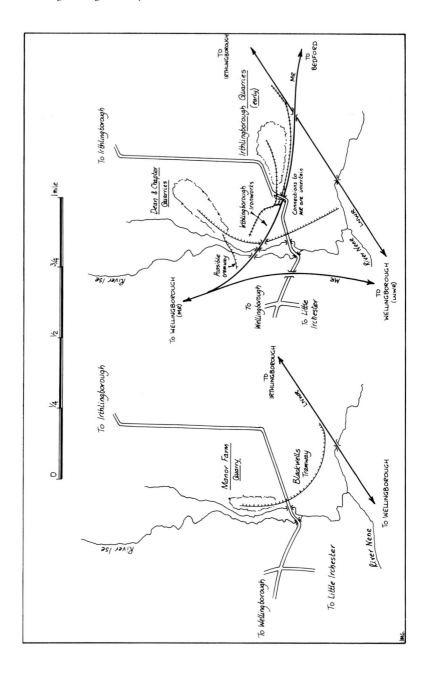

DEAN & CHAPTER QUARRIES

Owners: The Dean & Chapter of Peterborough Cathedral; Butlin Bevan & Co Ltd from 1870

These quarries are listed in MS for the period 1867–78, but it is necessary to make a few assumptions to justify continuity. For 1867–71 the location is given as 'Dean & Chapter Lands, Northampton', with the change of ownership to Butlin Bevan in 1870; and for 1872–78 as 'Dean & Chapter Lands, Irthlingborough'. The 'Northampton' of 1867–71 presumably refers to the county. Interpreted in this way, we get a logical sequence.

The precise location is not given, but there can be little doubt that the quarries were an extension of the Manor Farm Quarries. The Dean & Chapter had in 1852 been unhappy about allowing Blackwell & Smith to quarry on the land occupied by their tenant J.B. Howes; but times had changed – generally, ironstone quarries were being opened up wherever transport was available, and locally, Irthlingborough Ironworks on their land had started production in 1867. Ground to the north of Manor Farm Quarry was developed; for the first three years the Cathedral operated it themselves, probably by employing a contractor on the site, and then they passed the task on to Butlin Bevan & Co Ltd, already well experienced in these matters.

Once again, Midland Railway Deposited Plans come to our aid, this time those for the Bedford–Rushton Widening of November 1872; these show the original Manor Farm quarry site, now immediately to the north of the MR line, with a tramway passing under the latter to the level crossing with the Irthlingborough Road (Mill Road). The rest of the tramway is not shown, being outside the scope of the plan, but ownership of land and tramway is ascribed to Butlins. The 1884 OS shows the tramway in its complete form, much as in 1872 for the section north of the road, but south of the latter not curving east towards the LNWR but running in a straight line east by south to a wharf on the Nene. This surprising change of route probably dates back to about 1870. The Manor Farm pits lasted but a few years in the early 1850's and when they were closed the agreement with the LNWR would be rescinded; and when Irthlingborough Ironworks were built, standard gauge connections were made to the LNWR and MR, and the old Manor Farm line would no longer be required. We have no idea why it was reopened (perhaps even reinstated) with the route to the Nene Navigation; although published statistics record that a fairly large tonnage of iron ore was despatched from Dean & Chapter, we have no knowledge of ore being sent by river – but it might well have been the case. On the other hand, it is possible that the tramway was to bring in raw materials to the works from the river.

Having done a fair bit of guessing, let us do some more. Hudswell Clarke and Rodgers delivered locomotive No. 104, SAMSON, to 'T. Butlin, Wellingborough' in April 1871, to the curious gauge of 3ft 8¼ins. In general, locomotives were not built to such odd gauges other than to suit an existing tramway that had been built and equipped locally for horse traction without much regard for the future. So perhaps the Dean and Chapter line (and by implication Manor Farm also) was 3ft 8¼ins gauge, and Butlin Bevan adopted this gauge when setting up their narrow gauge system at Irchester. We think that HCR 104 worked at Irchester (opened for production in 1872) but she could have been tried out on the Nene tramway first. As stated, we are only guessing here and things could have been quite different; but these early obscure tramways stimulate the imagination, and we present our thoughts for consideration.

It is possible that these workings could be associated with the rather mysterious 'Smith's ironstone pits' that are mentioned in two newspaper reports for this period but otherwise seem to have escaped record. Characteristically, the news items are both of accidents; in the first,[1] "young labourer Timothy Peach at Mr Lowe Smith's ironstone pits at Wellingborough" attempted to get into a tub, but fell under it, while in the second[2] a man was injured whilst moving some wagons to the dock in "Mr Smith's iron pits near to the LNWR station at Wellingborough". These two accidents underline the casual attitude to health and safety then prevalent in industry, and for our purposes fix the location fairly closely and establish that a tramway was used. The location suggests that the quarry might be one of Butlin Bevans', a point established by further newspaper reports[3] of a court case of Lowe Smith v. Thos Butlin. Lowe Smith of Ringstead[4] was a contractor who had undertaken an ironstone contract for Butlins, using labourers mostly from Ringstead; he was trying to recover money for work done, not covered by his contract but which he had carried out before his contract had been terminated. This case presumably referred to another quarry (Ringstead?) operated by Smith for Butlin Bevan but it is clearly the same man in each case. The reports might equally refer to Butlin Bevans quarries at Dean & Chapter or at Little Irchester; and there we must leave it.

As with Manor Farm, the quarries have been built over and there is precious little to be seen of the tramway route towards the river; at the rear of the factory of Alf Meade (Wellingborough) Ltd there is a slight ridge in the flat ground, along the tramway route, and this ridge has been emphasised later by the building of a concrete culvert at one section. At the bank of the Nene, between the confluence with the Ise and the sluice (which was not there when the tramway existed) a wooden post in the river bank **might** be a relic of the wharf. That is all – but it is enough to make you ponder.

Footnotes

1.   *Northampton Mercury*, 27th September 1873.
2.   *Midland Free Press*, 3rd September 1876.
3.   *Kettering Leader* 20th June 1890 and 18th July 1890.
4.   Kelly's *Directory of Northamptonshire*, 1890.
I am indebted to Mick Dix and Roger West for these valuable newspaper references.

Grid References

908680	Quarry terminus
906677	End of line near Midland Railway
909671	Wharf on Nene

IRTHLINGBOROUGH OR WELLINGBOROUGH QUARRIES

Owners: Butlin, Bevan & Co Ltd; Thomas Butlin & Co Ltd from 27th June 1889; United Steel Cos Ltd from April 1920.

For the period 1863–66 MS lists both Butlin, Bevan & Co Ltd and G.E. Bevan & Co, as operating at Wellingborough; whether they had separate quarry systems, or were at independent quarries using a common tramway (Butlins and Stanton did this at Stantongate quarries; and Bevan and Pell also at Duston) is not known, but some sort of connection is implied by the coincidence of date and place; for 1867/8 nothing appears in the record, but from 1869 onwards Butlin, Bevan are given as operators. This may not even be the same site as the previous ones, but on balance probably was at least a reopening of the former Butlin, Bevan location. Again, the date coincides with the putting in blast of two more furnaces at Irthlingborough Ironworks, so that is probably where the bulk of the ore went, if not all of it.

The Dean & Chapter quarries already described were close to the ironworks but the map indications suggest that the ore from them was sent down the tramway to the Nene wharf for despatch elsewhere; but some ore may of course have been used on the spot. The quarries included under the heading of this section were further away from the ironworks. The straight section of Mill Road (the Wellingborough–Irthlingborough one) from the Ise crossing eastwards was realigned with two right-angle bends to cross the MR; not of much consequence at the time of limited road usage but a nuisance for present-day traffic. The Deposited Plans of the Midland Railway Bedford to Rushton Widening of November 1872 show a tramway, with a west-facing junction, to reach the ore in the ground between the old and new roads north of the MR. This can only have been a short-lived line, and our next information comes from the 1884 OS, which shows a longer line with an east-facing junction, in the reverse direction – towards the Ise and the old Dean & Chapter quarries site. This line had connections both to the LNWR and the MR, like the ironworks system.

Butlin's main quarrying area commenced on the spur of high ground north of the furnaces, in effect continuing north and east from the former Dean & Chapter quarries, and extending as far as the neighbourhood of South Hill Farm. They also worked on the east side of

Mill Road (Wellingborough–Irthlingborough) in the vicinity of Irthlingborough Grange, both north and south of the drive thereto, as indicated by the present-day level of the fields. There was also a working two thirds of a mile northeast of the Grange, south of Mill Road near South View Farm. Fuller details of these workings, or of the tramways serving them, have not survived.

Hudswell Clarke's records quote locomotive No. 86 (standard gauge) as delivered new in 1867 to 'Butlin Bevan & Co., Wellingborough' which would seem to qualify for this location; the small beginnings of 1863 being enlarged enough to require a locomotive, though production was not reported until 1869. There were some 3ft 8¼in gauge locomotives, also by Hudswell Clarke & Rodgers, that were supplied to 'T. Butlin, Wellingborough', and which we think must have been destined for Irchester; there were also three standard gauge locomotives from the same stable to the same ostensible destination in the same period, and these were almost certainly used at Irthlingborough Ironworks. The use of four or five at the ironworks tallies broadly with recollections of former employees (one stated that there were four at one time) and the requirements of the modest-sized plant. The later locomotives were presumably replacements.

The ironworks themselves were the property of Thomas Butlin & Co Ltd until taken over the United Steel Cos Ltd in April 1920. Rather surprisingly, United Steels reopened the quarrying area by obtaining from Wellingborough U.D.C. a lease of Spike Island, northeast of the furnaces between Mill Road and an area worked by Butlin's in the 1880's. The lease was dated 10th October 1922 and production seems to have commenced in March 1923.[1] The 1924 OS shows a tramway running north-north-east for half a mile from the works in the direction of Spike Island Cottage. Quarrying was soon to cease, however, as the ironworks was closed in 1925, the foundry continuing in operation and taken over in 1947 as Nuffield Foundry by Morris Motors Ltd, Engines Branch. Under the new management the factory was entirely reorganised, and traces of the early layout east of the works, where access to the ironstone was obtained, obliterated. Two of the former locomotives, both painted black with red coupling rods, remained at work until the arrival of a new Ruston & Hornsby diesel locomotive in 1955. The works later became part of the British Leyland Group as Wellingborough Foundries and was closed in September 1981.

The Ironworks site has been drastically altered of course, and the area close to the railway was levelled in 1985; but a possible terminal ironstone face is still visible on the east side of this cleared area. The other quarrying areas are denoted by fields sunk below road level, the best marked quarry being that on the south side of South Hill Farm, and the steep drop below road level on the south side of the Irthlingborough road almost opposite Sidegate Lane, at the rear of South View Farm.

Footnotes

1.   *Kettering Leader*, 9th June 1922; 13th October 1922; 27th April 1923.

Grid References

907676	Old standard gauge terminus
910675	Tipping dock at Ironworks
911684	Later terminus at Spike Island

Locomotive

Gauge; 4ft 8½ins

0-4-OST   OC   HCR 86   1867   10 x 16ins   2ft 9ins New 6/1867   s/s
The identity of this locomotive is assumed

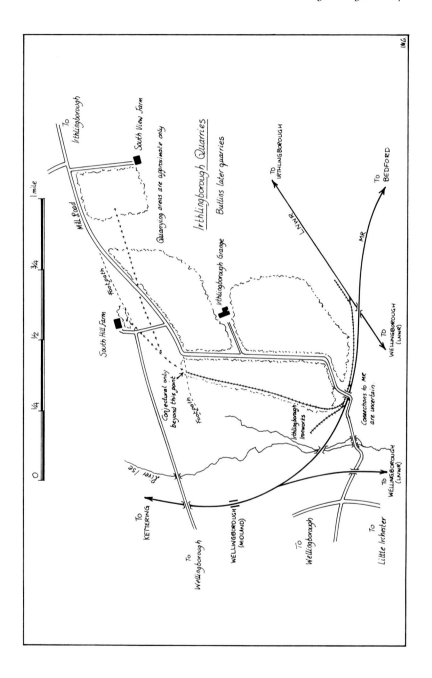

IRCHESTER QUARRIES

Owners: Butlin Bevan & Co Ltd.

Discovery of the tramway associated with these workings is due to the railway historian Geoffrey Webb in the course of researches into the Midland Railway, and who kindly brought it to our notice. The Deposited Plans of the Rushton & Bedford widening of November 1872 shows close to Irchester station a well-established system, which the plans of November 1875 show considerably modified and extended. The entry 'Irchester' in MS for 1872–75, hitherto attributed to the quarries associated with the LNWR, probably refer to the MR system, which did not last long and does not appear on the 1884 OS – which accounts for its having been overlooked for so long. However, armed with these clues, several other references came to light, particularly as the operations disturbed some Roman remains.

The MR 1872 map shows a simple tramway on the west side of the railway, running parallel to the main line from Irchester station, with branches to working faces, tipping docks at each end, and an engine shed, establishing that it was locomotive-worked. On the 1875 map the tipping docks have been replaced by connections to the MR, and the engine shed is in a different place, indicating a change in the interim to standard gauge; but at the point where the line crossed the footpath between Irchester and Knuston there is a building, with double tracks inside, captioned 'tramway shed and shutes', which we interpret as an end-on junction between narrow and standard gauges, with the former extending across the Higham Ferrers road to the Chester House area. This was reached in 1873, and quarrying exposed part of a Roman cemetery with some 300–400 skeletons, all facing east (a pagan, not Christian, custom). This of course immediately attracted the attention of archaeologists and historians, to whom we owe thanks for the extra information they provide. R.S. Baker[1] states that the workings were on the estate of R.W. Arkwright of Knuston Hall and the quarries were being worked by a firm of contractors, Lay & Clayson, on behalf of the lessees of the ground, Butlin Bevan &Co. In addition to the cemetery (which seems not to have been completely excavated, as it was on the edge of the outcrop) there were many other finds in 1873/4.

So much for the information provided by the archaeologists – and there is precious little else. Newspaper reports of accidents at 'Clayson's

Iron Pits' occur throughout the period 1870–78 so, assuming these all refer to Irchester, it seems that the quarries were operating earlier than indicated in MS (1872); there are several similar instances of this. A locomotive named SAMSON (HCR 104) to the curious gauge of 3ft 8¼ins was supplied by HCR in April 1871; an odd gauge like this is usually to be found on early self-built systems with horse traction, to which locomotives had to conform, and we wonder if in fact SAMSON went new to Irthlingborough for use on the tramway down to the Nene Wharf, that Butlin's had recently taken over, and then moved to Irchester? That it was at the latter site seems pretty certain in the absense of any other claimant; and in 1876 she was returned to the makers. By then the narrow gauge part of the system may have been horse-worked, but in any case we know it had gone by 1884, and perhaps some years before that. Much of this is pure conjecture, permissible in the absence of factual data. Of the locomotive used on the standard gauge line we are not even guessing; it could be any one from Irthlingborough Ironworks, or another one altogether.

There are few visible remains, as might be expected after over a century; there is not much near Irchester station site apart from a terminal face alongside a hedge, and some disturbed ground below road level, partly occupied by allotments on the northeast side of Chester Road (Irchester to the A 45). Cultivated ground on the southwest side of Chester Road at this point is also below road level, so possibly quarrying took place here, with a tramway extension over the road; but again we are guessing. Nothing is obvious near the curious double footbridge over the BR line, that was close to the exchange point. Beyond the A 45 the ground is sunk below road level, though how much of this is due to quarrying and how much to realignment of the A 45 is uncertain. Of the Roman cemetery there is nothing visible, and as the remains are not protected by the Department of the Environment they are not signposted.

Footnotes

1.   'Roman Remains at Irchester'. R.S. Baker, *Associated Architectural Societies Reports and Papers*. 1879–80 (XIII) p.89.

Grid References

926667	1872 Tipping dock to MR
931662	1872 Tipping dock to MR

929664	n.g locomotive shed
927666	1875 connection to MR
932660	1875 connection to MR
930660	s.g. locomotive shed
924670	Level crossing of Higham Ferrers road
922670	Face by Roman Cemetery site

Locomotive

Gauge; 3ft 8¼ins
SAMSON   0-4-OST   OC   HCR 104   1871   7 x 12ins   2ft 0ins   New 10/1915 (a)   (1)

(a) ex Dean & Chapter Quarries 1872 (?)

(1) returned to HCR 1876

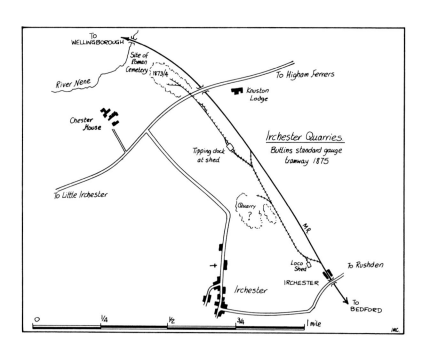

IRCHESTER QUARRIES

Owners: Butlin, Bevan & Co Ltd; Thomas Butlin & Co Ltd from 27th June 1889; James Pain Ltd from 1912; Irchester Ironstone Co Ltd from 8th June 1922; South Durham Steel & Iron Co Ltd from 3rd October 1953.

Butlin's activities at Wellingborough present, as we have seen, a rather tangled skein for the industrial archaeologist or historian to unravel; the overall picture is clear enough, but difficulty arises as soon as one tries to obtain greater detail. This is especially the case with the quarrying operations; a number of leases were negotiated with different landowners, but some without precise details of their location. Matters are not helped by the rather loose application of the name 'Wellingborough' to all and sundry locations, and the pooling of output statistics from more than one site. When we come to study Irchester, a similar problem arises, Butlins having two sets of workings served by separate tramways but not differentiated in MS.

According to MS, output at 'Irchester' commenced in 1872; we know that the tramway connected to the Midland Railway was in being in 1872, as it is shown on a MR plan dated November 1872. The first positive date for the quarry system served by the LNWR is 1875, when MS records output from Woolaston; the 1884 OS shows a branch from the Woolaston line to quarries near Little Irchester, but whether these were opened before or after Woolaston is unknown, as they are covered by the blanket entry 'Irchester'; but as they **were** on a branch, it seems rather more likely that they were opened up **after** Woolaston. A narrow gauge tramway was laid from a tipping dock erected over a couple of sidings at Wellingborough LNWR station, and ran due south for about one mile, crossing Rushden Road, Gipsy Lane and the drive to Little Irchester Lodge on the level. The branch towards the Irchester quarries turned off due east a quarter mile from the tipping dock. There is a possibility that Butlins worked also a small area west of London Road opposite the drive to Little Irchester Lodge, but whether this was reached by a branch crossing the main road or by horse and cart is unknown. By the time of the 1901 OS, the Woolaston line had been lifted beyond the junction to Irchester, while in the latter direction the tramway was considerably extended, with branches towards Rushden Road and Gipsy Lane.

There is no written record of the gauge or method of operation of the tramway, but an elderly employee at Nuffield Foundry, interviewed in the 1950's, stated that narrow gauge steam locomotives were used for the haulage of iron ore and limestone before 1900; and an employee at Irchester quarries recollected visiting the narrow gauge system as a child about 1905, when a steam locomotive known as 'the old coffee pot' was in use. Again, the OS map of 1884 shows at the junction of the branches to Irchester and Woolaston an 'engine shed', the existence of which was confirmed by the same informant. It seems likely that the four Hudswell Clarke & Rodgers locomotives of 3ft 8¼ins gauge supplied to T. Butlin & Co, Wellingborough in 1874–6 were for this system, the odd gauge adopted being the same as at the other 'Irchester' quarries, as described under the previous heading. We have also discussed earlier the possible origin of this rare gauge; one can speculate in this way and find answers that suit the known data, but with so much still unknown it is not a wise exercise. 'The old coffee pot', for example, often signifies a vertical-boilered locomotive, of which there may have been an example as well as the Hudswells; but the term has been applied to oldfashioned locomotives of orthodox design also. **The** surprising thing is that the whole locomotive stock (other than those disposed of earlier) vanished apparently without trace when only a mere thirty years old, for there is no record of one making an appearance elsewhere; it seems certain that by 1900 only one, or possibly two, engines remained. And there it seems we shall have to leave the locomotive side. The wagons were wooden end-tippers, according to Hewlett. 1895 was the last year of production at Woolaston in Butlin's day, but Irchester quarries continued until 1903, and the tramway was lifted then or shortly afterwards.

In addition to ironstone, limestone was also worked at a site southeast of Poplar Barn, and after Butlins had ceased operations here James Pain obtained limestone for the two years 1905/6, presumably from the same site; so it is not surprising to learn that a few years later he recommenced ironstone working at Irchester. There were two leases, both in Irchester parish and both for a term of 30 years from 31st December 1911. The principal one was with Lady Wantage for 353 acres; but the smaller lease for about 30 acres is perhaps the more interesting as being granted by 'The King's Most Excellent Majesty'. How this small parcel of land immediately to the east of Little Irchester village came into royal hands is not clear. Between them the two leases extended from the river Nene eastwards between Rushden Road and Gipsy Lane almost as far as Irchester. Butlins presumably had a lease of this area too, but details have not survived.

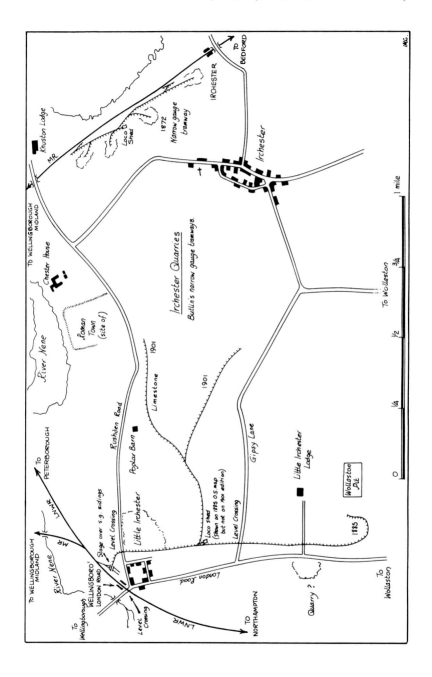

There was little similarity to Butlin's doubtless archaic quarry system in the new setup. Pain, in his characteristic thoroughgoing fashion, laid a standard gauge line and introduced steam diggers in the quarry, as he had at Glendon. These policies were typical of James Pain, and as this is our first introduction to him, one of the outstanding personalities of the ironstone industry a few asides on his character and influence will be in order. 'Jimmy' Pain came from Oakley, near Corby, but had family connections with Desborough, and it was here that he started his career in the ironstone industry; another venture at Corby was more ambitious but his real chance came with the failure of the Glendon Iron Co Ltd, when he acquired their extensive ironstone properties at Glendon, and applied to them the advantages of steam locomotives and quarry machines, some of which he had probably seen in action at Lloyd's Ironstone Co Ltd at Corby. This policy of modernisation brought its reward in reduced costs and increased business and soon Pain (as James Pain Ltd, registered in September 1905) was opening entirely new fields in practically virgin territory, as at Market Overton and Uppingham. He refused to enter the ironmaking business, however, and remained faithful to quarrying throughout.

James Pain Senior had four sons, James William, Gordon Harold, Douglas Wheeler and Lance, all of whom at one time or another were in charge of the several quarries; James William (known as Will) was manager at Irchester, but about 1913 he left the company to set up in the same line of business on his own at Whiston and later at Byfield and Bloxham, with assistance from his younger brother Lance. Gordon and Douglas Pain carried on as Directors of James Pain Ltd; the former was in charge of the Uppingham workings at the time Will was in command at Irchester. James Pain Sr died 3rd January 1913, aged 63. The intensified demand of the war years called for further extensions but after that the company gradually disposed of its properties, closing the poorly productive ones (e.g. Uppingham) and selling the others to larger concerns, finally disposing of the remaining pits to Stanton Ironworks Co Ltd in 1928.

Between 1912 and 1922 James Pain Ltd 'built up a strong position by leases and purchase of land' as Hewlett puts it, such that he was able in the period of reduced demand after World War I to sell Irchester as a going concern. The new owner was Irchester Ironstone Co Ltd, a company controlled by Cargo Fleet Iron Co Ltd, but in which James Pain Ltd held 3000 preference shares, which entitled Gordon and Douglas

Pain to seats on the board. The 1912 leases referred to above were assigned to Irchester Ironstone Co Ltd for the remainder of the term, and James Pain Ltd owned portions of land that were leased to the new company, and these arrangements continued until James Pain Ltd were taken over in 1928 by Stanton Ironworks Co Ltd, Stanton becoming both a lessor to, and part proprietor of, Irchester Ironstone Co Ltd. Management was however in the hands of Cargo Fleet through a local mining engineer. Also in 1928, Cargo Fleet became a subsidiary of South Durham Steel & Iron Co Ltd, and when the latter opened Storefield quarries, there was pooling of certain facilities such as major locomotive and machinery repairs. The 1912 leases were surrendered in 1937 and replaced by new ones for 25 years 9 months from 1st April 1937. It is interesting to note that the royalties on the Wantage lease were $2\frac{5}{8}$ pence (raw) and $3\frac{1}{2}$ pence (calcined), while on the King's lease the figures were $\frac{3}{4}$ and $1\frac{1}{2}$ pence.

As already mentioned, James Pain installed a standard gauge railway system to serve the quarries and at the same time he eliminated the level crossing of the Rushden road; instead, the line tunneled beneath the road ('Clarke's Bridge') followed by a stiffish bank in cutting. Short sharp banks seemed to be a characteristic of James Pain's quarry tramways, making them at once a headache to the operating staff and a joy to the steam locomotive enthusiast. By the bridge was a weigh-house and near the top of the cutting was built a long single-road engine shed, with louvres in the roof instead of 'pots' (Pain's Glendon North shed had a louvre, too) and a small fitting shop of corrugated iron behind it. Beyond this the line ran southeast, still climbing, to the main quarry area. The quarries could be regarded as extensions of Butlin's old workings, including ground immediately east of Little Irchester (called the King pit for obvious reasons) and penetrating further east towards Irchester village and south towards Gipsy Lane under deeper cover.

There were also quarries north of Rushden Road, served by a separate tramway leaving the LNWR goods yard in an easterly direction via a gate; and as these were comparatively short-lived we will deal with them now. NSI implies that these pits were operated in the time of James Pain Ltd, who found the stone rather silicious, but on the LMSR station diagram dated October 1926 the rail connection is endorsed 'To New Quarry; Agreement 1st May 1925'. It is probable that the lease was negotiated by James Pain, but working delayed by the slump in the industry until his successors took over. Full details of the lease have not come to light, but

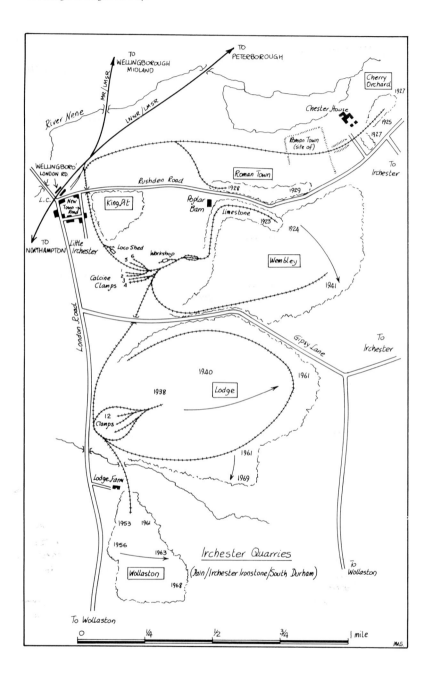

TO
WELLINGBOROUGH
MIDLAND

TO
PETERBOROUGH

Cherry
Orchard
1927

River Nene

MR/LMSR

LNWR/LMSR

Chester House

1925

Roman Town
(site of)

1927

WELLINGBORO'
LONDON RD

To
Irchester

Roman Town

Rushden Road

1928

1929

L.C.

New
Town
Road

King Pit

Poplar
Barn

Limestone
1923

1924

TO
NORTHAMPTON

Little
Irchester

Loco Shed
5
6

Workshop

Wembley

1941

Calcine
Clamps
1
2
3
4

Gipsy Lane

To
Irchester

London Road

1940

Lodge

1961

1938

12
Clamps

1961

1961

1969

Lodge Farm

1953 1961

1956

1963

Irchester Quarries

To
Wollaston

Wollaston

1968

(Pain/Irchester Ironstone/South Durham)

To Wollaston

0   ¼   ½   ¾   1 mile

IMG.

Irchester Quarries. South portal of the bridge under the A 45 at Little Irchester. The signal controlling the branch can be seen in the distance. 23rd May 1960.   G.H. Starmer

Irchester Quarries. Hawthorn Leslie, No 17, dropping its fire at the shed, 21st June 1967. Note the worked-out area in the background.   Ian L. Wright

a plan in BSC archives has marked on it an area of about 200 acres extending eastwards from Little Irchester, north of Rushden Road to the hedge between Chester House and the MR main line, and a strip south of the road from Poplar Barn to Chester Road. On this plan the lessor is given as 'Robb and Caulfield' and the area south as 'Parson's Farm', which was part of the Wantage lease. Dr W.W. Robb was closely involved; he was present when the tramway was taken across the Roman Town site, and describes the finds there;[1] and Jack Roberts remembers him as the landowner, as the quarrymen had to chalk 'R' on wagons filled from the northern perimeter of the Wembley pit (see below), the rest of this pit being on the Wantage lease. Presumably too he was the W. Robb who in 1917 leased ground near Finedon to Ebbw Vale Steel Iron & Coal Co Ltd.

Jack Roberts, who had a phenomenal memory, stated that the tramway was put in in 1926, work ceasing at the time of the General Strike in May, and recommencing some nine months later. He too remembered the Roman finds, including coffins, one of which held the skeleton of a man nearly seven feet tall; this or another one was sent away to a museum in an improvised hearse consisting of a wagon partly filled with ore, with more ore piled on afterwards. Presumably this was just to serve as packing material, and we hope the whole load was not consigned to the furnace! The tramway extended to the limit of the lease, obliquely crossing the Roman Town site in Borough Close, and cutting through the west and east ramparts, then on a low embankment towards a level crossing with the avenue to Chester House and in shallow cutting beyond this. Working commenced in 1927 to the east of Chester House in a north-south gullet that evidently proved abortive, and the Cherry Orchard pit at the furthest point of the leased area was opened up later in the same year, working south to north; but here again it was not very successful and work ceased probably just over a year later. A No. 12 steam digger transferred from Desborough was used for loading, driven by Jack. Operations were transferred to a new quarry alongside Rushden Road (the A 45) called Roman Town quarry, though in fact it did not encroach on the Town proper; it was served by a branch tramway and was worked 1929–30 with a No. 10 digger loading, the overburden being removed by hand. There was a fair amount of clay mixed with the stone, and attempts to remove this by hand from the wagons were not completely successful. The 'Chester House' group of quarries were then closed, and work concentrated on the big Wembley pit south of Rushden Road. The tramway was lifted, of course.

Irchester Quarries.   MAUD running back to the empty wagon sidings at the BR junction, 23rd May 1969. Note (left) the connection to the main BR line; and (right) a very short siding that is probably the stub of the lengthy line to the Roman Town and Cherry Orchard quarries.   G.H. Starmer

Irchester Quarries.   A 1927 view of the 'King' pit – so named as the ground was leased from the Sovereign. The RP shovel (RP 446) was bought new by James Pain from an engineering exhibition, in 1916. She is a 20-ton machine.   Collection M.C. Fayers

South of Rushden Road work had been continuing in the King pit and further east. A No 12 Ruston Proctor steam navvy came here new (bought by Pain at an engineering exhibition) in 1916, replaced by a new 20-ton machine six years later. Arthur Hopkins was the senior machine driver and Jack Roberts learnt a great deal from him; in addition to driving, Arthur was a wizard in looking after and rebuilding machines, and Jack recalls his expertise with a couple of poles in lieu of lifting cranes. On the closure of Twywell quarries in 1924, their machines were transferred to Irchester, and Jack took part in the move of the No. 10 Ruston, said to be the first caterpillar-tracked machine in the ironstone fields; the move took place on 4th September 1924, starting at 5.0 am and travelling through Finedon and Wellingborough centre, as Eastfield Road and the Embankment were not in existence then.

The production of limestone from the area near Rushden Road appears to have ceased, possibly in Pain's day, but certainly under Cargo Fleet, who could doubtless obtain supplies nearer their furnaces; and, soon after the change of ownership, ironstone was obtained mostly from one long face extending in a widening and deepening arc from near Rushden Road to near Gipsy Lane. This was known as the Wembley pit, as production began in 1924, at the time of the Empire Exhibition; the first machine on the site was a new 20-ton Ruston with a long jib and on caterpillar tracks. There were soon greatly improved facilities on this side. About 1929, at the summit of the bank a half mile from the LMSR junction, commodious new workshops were erected for the repair of quarry machinery and locomotives. The necessity for these shops was occasioned by increased mechanisation; in Pain's day, according to GSM, only the overburden was removed by navvy, the ore being dug out by hand and sold in the raw state to customers chiefly in the Midlands. Under Cargo Fleet management the bulk of the ore was destined for the company's furnaces in the northeast, and the practice of calcining was introduced to reduce freight charges; further, the quarries, as exemplified by the Wembley Pit, were becoming very much deeper. The overburden was removed by a Ruston No 300 shovel with a $5\frac{1}{2}$ cubic yard capacity bucket and a 90-foot jib, capable of dealing with depths up to 55 feet; the underlying ironstone was blasted and then loaded by Ruston shovels into side-tipping wagons and taken to a fan of six calcine clamps close to the workshops. Extra locomotives were required to handle trains from the quarry, marshall wagons for the clamps, and take the calcined ore to the LMSR; and small steam cranes were needed at the clamps as well as in the quarry.

Irchester Quarries. Lodge pit was very deep, with a steep bank up to field level. Our picture shows No 17 (HL 3892) blasting its way up to the sidings on 23rd March 1967.

G.D. King

The Wembley pit was worked clockwise southwards up to 1941, after which the rail tracks were lifted. The older worked-out portions of the quarry were left by the travelling shovel in the familiar hill-and-dale formation that it was impracticable to restore; this was mostly on Stanton's freehold property, and they afforested the area with larch and pine, as was their custom. Hence, though the quarries nominally belonged to South Durham Steel & Iron Co Ltd, these restored areas bear the imprint of Stanton's methods.

As the Wembley pit was nearing exhaustion, the Irchester Lodge pit was reopened, again as an extension of an old Butlin's quarry area under thicker cover. A branch line was constructed in late 1936, leaving the existing 'main line' by a trailing junction near the workshops, running southwesterly in a cutting and passing beneath Gipsy Lane by a concrete bridge towards London Road, thence roughly following the course of the former narrow gauge system. It then turned east to Lodge pit, so-called from the then demolished Little Irchester Lodge, where production commenced in July 1937. A Ransomes & Rapier 5360 Stripping Shovel was obtained to deal with the overburden of 60 feet or more in this very deep quarry between Gipsy Lane and the valley south of the Lodge, in which wagons and locomotives looked like toys to the spectator on the brink. As at the Wembley pit, calcining was the practice, but in this case the six clamps were placed near the quarry entrance.

The Wantage lease included about 30 acres of ground west of London Road, where the ironstone was under shallow cover, and in the 1940's a proposal was made to work this, carrying the output by an aerial ropeway to the main site; but permission to cross the busy London Road by this means was refused, not surprisingly. Instead, leases were obtained to work further south, towards Woolaston; these included 46 acres of Lodge Farm (Indenture 28th June 1948) and a larger area from the Ecclesiastical Commissioners. A three-quarter mile extension of the tramway was constructed in 1952, in the course of which some buried narrow gauge rails (from Butlin's day) were found.[2] The new quarry lay about half a mile from Woolaston village. Track south of Gipsy Lane was chaired, elsewhere flat-bottomed, with tie-bars in position where required to preserve alignment.

By the outbreak of World War II operations were concentrated on the newly-opened Lodge pit, and this set the pattern for the remainder of the working life of the Irchester system. Calcining was standard practice, the ore being loaded into 'Gloucester' wagons supplied by Gloucester Railway

Carriage & Wagon Co Ltd, and similar in pattern to 'dumpcars' used at other quarries; from them the ore was tipped on to the clamps and after burning and cooling was loaded into railway wagons, mostly 27-ton 'Iron Ore Tipplers'. This was a very dirty job, as Mr Williams (who worked at Irchester 1919 to 1969) recalls, the men going home at the end of the day 'looking like Red Indians'. It could be dangerous too; during the war there was a temptation to shift the calcine before it was properly cooled, and one man at least was badly burnt this way.

In earlier days, at Wembley pit, wooden side-tipping wagons of 'Manchester Ship Canal' type were employed, and a number of these survived near the old calcine clamps by the workshops until the closure. The bodies of these wagons were mainly constructed by Watts Hardy & Co Ltd of Newcastle-upon-Tyne, and Jack Roberts remembers them being supplied new to Irchester. Most of the locomotives were fitted with combination buckeye and link couplings for handling respectively the 'Gloucesters' and 'Tipplers', but PROGRESS and 15 had link couplings only and their duties were limited accordingly. When calcining ceased (in 1961 it is believed) the necessity for locomotives to have buckeye couplings ceased, and later arrivals were not so fitted.

One locomotive worked in the quarry, taking ore to the calcining clamps; another took the 'burnt' ore to the sidings near the workshops, where a third locomotive backed on to the other end and took the train to the BR sidings, leaving the other engine to return to the pit for the next load, picking up empty wagons on the way. The BR job was often allocated to a locomotive with link couplings only. When Woolaston pit was opened, it had its own locomotive working to the sidings by London Road (near the entrance to Lodge pit); there were then four locomotives in steam, sometimes five if the demand was heavy. Lodge pit was in the form of a crescent, with the face on the outer edge, progressing eastwards, and finally with a section to the south. Woolaston pit was worked in strips, again from west to east.

The locomotives were a very mixed bag indeed and with three exceptions were obtained secondhand; the dates of their acquisition complement nicely the history of quarry development. James Pain made do with two locomotives as far as we know; DAISY was the first arrival, coming from Pain's Corby quarries, and is remembered for an eccentricity recalled by Mr B.H. Maycock – "This engine could only be driven satisfactorily by one particular driver and it was found that his secret of 'successful' working was due to his placing large pieces of clay

Irchester Quarries. The Peckett six-wheeler PROGRESS (P 1402) formerly at the Desborough 'Co op' quarries, was photographed on 29th July 1952 at the foot of the calcine bank. Note wagon on the top. G.H. Starmer

Irchester Quarries. Not all of the locomotives came from the northeast. This neat little Peckett ROTHWELL (P 1258) was new to the ironstone industry and came to Irchester under the ownership of James Pain. She received her name when working at Glendon. 16th April 1938. G. Alliez/Courtesy B.D. Stoyel

around the tip of the blastpipe, thereby obstructing the exhaust and creating a sharper draught through the fire". In parentheses it should be mentioned here that Mr. Upchurch (who in 1961 had served in the quarries for 47 years) stated that DAISY was the last remaining locomotive on the narrow gauge, as he remembered it. Accepting both versions, DAISY was the last narrow gauge and the first standard gauge engine; obviously there might be some confusion of identity here, but there **could** have been two locos of the same name. But there is no doubt of the standard gauge DAISY at Corby. ROTHWELL came from Glendon quarries – a nice example of earlyish Peckett with a polished brass dome and spring-balance safety valves.

The next five locomotives were acquired to cover the extra duties demanded by longer quarry lines and the introduction of calcining. The most unusual – and least successful – was ANCOATS, a standard Manning Wardle 0-4-0ST rebuilt in 1922 by Blackwell's of Northampton with a vertical boiler and horizontal geared engine from a Sentinel steam lorry, the work being carried out under the direction of Mr. K.W. Willans. The locomotive was not powerful enough for the work at Irchester and was soon disposed of, but the principle was considered to be sound and Willans joined the Sentinel staff; in 1924 the locomotive was sent to the Sentinel shops for rebuilding with a custom-built vertical boiler (No 5666) and was then sold to Thos E. Gray Ltd at Burton Latimer.

Three more locomotives were obtained to operate the new Lodge pit, when the necessity for reversal at the workshops area entailed more motive power. Subsequent locomotives were obtained to operate Wollaston pit and, later, to replace earlier ones withdrawn and again were mainly 'throw-outs' from the North-east. Mention of these will arise when we come to discuss latterday operations in more detail, but at this point we should refer to the titling of locomotives, on the face of it rather haphazard but in fact attended by care to avoid ambiguity in the records of the boiler inspector. Mr. W.A. Brown, the plant superintendent, explained the system; "the answer is a matter of the British Insurance Co. I found it rather a nuisance to have a number so and so loco with a different number on the Boiler Report. Our insurance office at Cargo Fleet and the Scottish Boiler Insurance at Glasgow did not want to change their records. It was not until the number 300 Excavator came that I was able to make a start" This excavator became No. 14 in the boiler records – there being in existence at Irchester at that time five locomotives (ROTHWELL, PROGRESS, COCKSPUR, No 1 and 11) and eight quarry machines (Rustons 446. 509/13/25. 730/78/79. 814.) New locomotives HL 3892 and 3946 became 15 and 17, whilst the Chapman & Furneaux that arrived between the two became 16. 17 had a Hawthorn Leslie type of numberplate fitted to the engine when delivered but 15 and 16 had rather ornate numberplates, probably cast at Irchester. Nos 18–20 were allocated to the next three locomotives acquired by South Durham for ironstone work, at Irchester or Storefield, though in fact 18 never carried this number. After 1950 this numbering scheme seems to have been abandoned. According to Andrew Barclay records, 19 was ordered for Storefield quarries, but she was diverted, possibly for production reasons, to Irchester for a couple of years.

The next six arrivals retained their names or numbers, but with AB 1609 we come to another little mystery. On arrival in February 1959 she sported a cast plate lettered SOUTH DURHAM STEEL & IRON CO LTD 1918, but afterwards new plates No. 8 were made – cast by May 1959 but not fitted immediately. They were exceptionally neat little plates, of bronze (not brass) with characters incised and filled with black enamel. The choice of number was explained as being that on the insurance policy; and we find that AB 1609 was the eighth locomotive purchased by the Seaton Carew Iron Co Ltd, and was the last one before the company was absorbed by South Durham. There was one other oddity; when AB 2323 came from Lackenby she carried 6 on cabside plates, but as Irchester already had a No. 6, the new arrival was altered to 9 by turning the plate upside down! The engine was working so numbered on the day after arrival.

The locomotives, while a varied lot, were (except for ANCOATS) in general standard products of well-known makers, but a few acquired special features in the way that industrials do. Liveries did not vary much however, the standard in the post World War II period being green with red rods – through not always the same green. MAJOR and 1918 were in a light green and also had red valances, red hand rails and green wheels, though MAJOR was repainted in the standard livery in 1960. 15 and No. 17 were received new in green lined black edged yellow, with red rods, and No. 17 ended its day so; but 15, which also originally had the valances red, lined black edged yellow, received the standard style of painting in 1956. There were variants; ROTHWELL had grey side rods, and HOLWELL NO. 30 had red handrails when repainted in 1965. ROTHWELL and PROGRESS had green-backed brass nameplates. Finally, later arrivals 7 and 9 came in a livery of black, lined yellow, with yellow side rods and bufferbeams; while diesel MAUD retained its smart

Irchester Quarries. These quarries were characterised by a remarkable variety of locomotives, the majority of which were secondhand and retaining features of their origin. Chapman & Furneaux 1195 is shown out of use on 24th April 1958 at the reversing point beyond the sheds, with a background of larches on 'hill and dale' on Wembley pit. She came from the north-east, like several others. G. Alliez/Courtesy B.D. Stoyel

Irchester Quarries. An Andrew Barclay locomotive of latterday working; No. 8, or 1918, per plates on the cabside. She is AB 1609, photographed 14th June 1962. Note the dumb buffers. S.A. Leleux

Oxfordshire Ironstone livery of maroon, lined black edged yellow. The numbers appeared in various places – No. 9 on the lower cab sheet, No. 6, 11, 15, 16, 19 on the upper panels, and No. 17 on the tank, for examples.

Special features among the stock were as follows:- 16 had only steam brake. MAJOR and 1918 had dumb buffers originally, but MAJOR received the buffers off No. 9; 7 and 9 (AB 2324/3) had spring-loaded dumb buffers. No. 14 and No. 6 were fitted with steel ladders to help in tank filling. No. 17 was rebuilt in 1959 with a boiler slightly shorter than the original, so that the saddle tank overhung the smokebox. Also, from 1965–67 she ran with the right hand front buffer missing!

It was planned to rebuild PROGRESS with a Barclay boiler, but when she was stripped down for this in 1963 it was found very difficult to fit the boiler, and the project was abandoned when HOLWELL No. 30 arrived. 9 (AE 1797) was stripped down to frame and wheels only, and the connecting rods removed, so that the frame could be used for carrying excavator buckets etc. Similarly, a rake of three wooden wagons had their tops removed and were used for carrying jibs etc. Six-wheelers were not favoured; No. 6 indeed was said to be less powerful than HOLWELL NO. 30, which could handle twelve loaded wagons to the BR sidings.

As already indicated, our knowledge of the quarry machines at Irchester is unusually good; this is largely due to there being on hand one of the foremost enthusiasts in this field, Marshall Fayers, who obtained information from friends at the quarries (B.H. Maycock and others) and Mr W.A. Brown, the plant superintendent in Cargo Fleet days and the possessor of a phenomenal memory for numbers and events. This description applied equally to Jack Roberts, whom we have mentioned several times; he was sixteen at the time of the move of the No. 10 machine from Twywell to Irchester in September 1924, and his memories are very vivid. From these sources it has been possible to compile a record that is probably more complete than for almost any other ironstone quarry, certainly as far as steam is concerned. Steam machines were in operation at Irchester later than in most ironstone quarries, and included some working well into the 1960's. The machines came in threes from various sources; three were taken over from James Pain in 1922, then three new machines were purchased from Ruston & Hornsby. These were followed by three more from the closed Twywell quarries, and finally three secondhand, two from Desborough quarries and one from an outside contractor. Of these, 525 was used on the calcine bank. There was only one other steam machine after this – but this was something special, the 300 type, the

Irchester Quarries. 15 (HL 3892) was one of the few locomotives that came to Irchester new, and is here seen in her original livery on 16th April 1938.

Irchester Quarries. Among the later acquisitions were two 1952 Barclays transferred from West Hartlepool. Shown is 7, AB 2324, photographed from London Road on 27th February 1967. J.R. Bonser

Irchester Quarries. The solitary Bagnall, ENTERPRISE, approaches the yard with a rake of tipplers, with the roperunner dealing with the couplings. June 1966.

Ian L. Wright

largest steam navvy built by Rustons. After service at Irchester, she was dismantled and re-erected at Storefield (Newton pit). Later machines, most of which were electric, came new from the makers, Ruston Bucyrus or Ransomes & Rapier, as far as is known. The most familiar of these was the 5360 stripping shovel that spent the whole of its working life at Lodge pit, and was a familiar sight in photographs of this deep quarry, and was visible (in part anyway) from London Road. She finished at the end of 1967, having literally worked herself to death. Her last working date was reported as 29th December by Geoffrey Starmer, who photographed her that Friday; the survey plans quote 2nd January 1968.

Loading of ironstone was at first by steam machine, then others, including a 43RB diesel digger and a 55RB electric shovel, both by Ruston Bucyrus; there were also two Ransomes & Rapier 480 type electric shovels. Lodge pit was also the repository for many years of a collection of discarded locomotive boilers – there were three in 1962, two Barclays and one Hawthorn Leslie – and other oddments, e.g. a saddle tank, cab and parts of No. 9. Possibly a steam crane had been used to lift the boilers out of the frames, as was sometimes done by the machine at the calcine bank near the workshops.

It will be clear that Irchester was an interesting system to see at work; plenty of locomotives and quarry machines in action, and a very real 'atmosphere'. For one thing, they were very self-sufficient; with the 'headquarters' so far away, they had to be. And the workshops, well equipped in the 1920's, could be described forty years later as 'of great historical interest' (if you were an industrial archaeologist) or 'archaic' (if you had to use the machines). Yet in spite of these limitations the staff did very well indeed, keeping the locomotives on the road and maintaining the required output. There were no new locomotives after 1937, but no shortage of secondhand ones that they had finished with up north and gradually the area round Irchester shops came to look as if Colonel Stephens himself were in charge; four locomotives at work, two spare or under repair, and perhaps six in various stages of decay. The supernumerary locomotives were kept mainly as a source of spares, it seems, and even then were not left in peace, but were shunted around the premises from time to time, occupying at various times the stump of a 1955 temporary line, a siding by the calcine bank, the reversing sidings, and a line outside the shops.

The number of steam locomotives existing in each year during the two decades summarises the story: 1950/1 – 5: 1952–6 – 6: 1957/8 – 8: 1959 – 9:

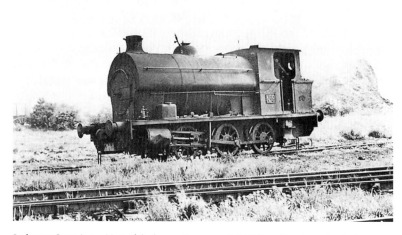

Irchester Quarries. Most of the locomotives were 0-4-OST but this photograph shows one of the six-wheelers, No. 9, AE 1787 on 23rd May 1957. Behind her is the bank of calcined ore.   G. Alliez/Courtesy B.D. Stoyel

Irchester Quarries. HOLWELL No. 30 (HL 3780) with a heavy train of empties coming up the bank to the reversing point, 2nd June 1966.   P.H. Groom

Irchester Quarries. Irchester was famous for its wealth of steam quarry machines, which lasted longer than at most ironstone quarries. Shown here is the No. 12 Ruston shovel loading at the calcine bank, 5th April 1967. J.R. Bonser

1960/1 – 10: 1962 – 11: 1963 – 12: 1964/5 – 13: 1966 – 12: 1967 – 9: 1968 – 6: 1969 – 7.

Locomotives acquired in the late 1950's were chiefly to meet the extra power required by the opening of Woolaston pit, and by 1960 there were ten locomotives to cover a maximum of five duties. The cessation of calcining simplified the work in that 'tipplers' were then loaded at the pit face for transit to the sidings without transhipment, but the pattern of locomotive operation remained much the same, with an engine in each pit working to the sidings by London Road, where another locomotive took over, and yet another from the works area to BR. The accumulated calcined ore was also disposed of, sometimes to cover temporary breakdowns in normal production. The arrival of HOLWELL No. 30 in 1963, and of 6 (alias 9) and 7 in 1964 – three good engines – made with No. 14 and No. 17 a fine team, leaving No. 6 (AB 1497) as a spare; and at long last five of the sorry collection of decaying relics were sold for scrap. Incidentally, there had been some suggestion of buying redundant steamers from Oxfordshire Ironstone, but nothing came of this. With the simplified stock position, drivers and locomotives tended to keep to the

51

same duties, e.g. No. 14 – Woolaston pit: No. 16 – Lodge pit: 9 – working to works yard: HOLWELL No. 30 – working to BR, who collected trainloads thrice daily.

At the end of 1967 rumours of closure were in the air, not surprisingly in view of the spate of closures in the 1960's; and sure enough the announcement was made that production would cease on 1st March 1968. The manager, Mr. Carden, tried very hard to get this rescinded, and his perseverance met with success – "the best news I've had for years" was how he put it. Woolaston pit, which was nearly exhausted, would close as planned, but Lodge pit would be kept open. The changed decision came about "largely as a result of the effects of devaluation, and the need to use as much home ore as possible consistent with economic working" – to quote the official BSC statement. Seventeen men out of the workforce of fifty were made redundant. On the locomotive side, 7, 9, No. 17 and HOLWELL No. 30 were to be kept.

Before the threatened shutdown output had been around 300,000 tons per year (during World War II it was twice that amount) but afterwards fell, as would be expected, to about 200,000 tons. Some quarry equipment was transferred from Wollaston to Lodge pit. Only two locomotives were in use, one in the pit and the other working through to BR. A further steam locomotive was obtained in August 1968, a Kitson displaced by dieselisation at Glendon. Though a bit on the heavy side for Irchester's

Irchester Quarries. Lodge pit, showing the great depth of overburden that had to be tackled by the 5360 stripping shovel at right. A 43RB levels the deposited material to the left, and in the pit a R&R shovel is at the ironstone face. No. 17 is the locomotive standing by. 23rd July 1952.   S.A. Leleux

Irchester Quarries. The big steamer in Wembley pit, about 1935. This was the largest steam shovel in the ironstone fields and was built in 1930 by Ruston & Hornsby. She finished her days at Storefield Quarries.

Collection Bob Smith

ageing track, she was a powerful machine and enabled some of the hard-worked four-wheelers to be pensioned off; the Manning Wardle was stored at the shed with sacking over the chimney, as preservationists were interested in acquiring her.

South Durham Steel & Iron Co Ltd was amalgamated with Stewarts & Lloyds Ltd and Dorman Long & Co Ltd on 22nd June 1967, Dorman Long becoming the British Steel & Tube Co Ltd, with the other two as subsidiaries. This company was taken over by the British Steel Corporation on 23rd June 1968, but SDSI retained its identity until the Corporation's reorganisation of 29th March 1970. The move of CARMARTHEN arose from the amalgamation of SDSI and S&L interests, which was evinced also in the introduction of 'plant numbers' for the locomotives and other things. CARMARTHEN carried its own number 8310/54 and others noted were: 9 – 8310/26: 7 – 8310/27: No. 17 – 8310/29: HOLWELL No. 30 – 8310/32 (this loco had formerly carried 9411/60 from its Holwell days). Looking forward, diesel MAUD was 8411/06, allotted at Market Overton.

In January 1969 traffic diminished again, requiring only one locomotive in service (usually CARMARTHEN, sometimes HOLWELL No. 30); and a diesel locomotive was promised. This came from Market Overton in the following month, replaced there by another from the same stable, Oxfordshire Ironstone Co Ltd. If 24 wagons were ordered the diesel alone was used; if 36, HOLWELL No. 30 (which had received a new set of tubes in the autumn of 1968) was used in the quarry, with the diesel working to BR, taking eight wagons at a time; but by the beginning of April, MAUD was doing the lot. Refuelling from a 45-gallon drum was a cumbersome job requiring the services of three or four men for some twenty minutes, but in May 1969 the structure for a new oil tank was being constructed on the siding to the workshops. It was never completed, alas, as closure – permanent this time – was announced to the staff of 28 on May 14th. It was pointed out that even at the present reduced output the quarries only had three years of life, and the ore was not suitable for the steelmaking process adopted at the new Scunthorpe works; and the old Hartlepool and Cargo Fleet works that Irchester had supplied since 1922 were to be gradually phased out. The plant was closed officially on 6th June, and track-lifting started immediately – but on Monday 9th June instructions were given to replace the lifted track, as a fortnight's reprieve had come with a demand for thirty wagon loads per day for one week, and twenty a day for the second week. Final closure was

Irchester Quarries. A rake of dumpcars being loaded by a 480 R&R shovel in Wembley pit. c.1935. Locomotive is presumed to be COCKSPUR. Fred Whitehead; Collection Bob Smith.

Irchester Quarries. With their miscellany of second-hand locomotives, often rebuilt in their own shops with parts from others, Irchester quarries assumed a 'Colonel Stephens' atmosphere. There were usually several derelicts on the premises, a position accentuated towards the end of operations – as here on 2nd June 1966. Right to left are HL 3780, P 1258, AB 1363, AB 1609 and P 1402. P.H. Groom

Irchester Quarries.   Another batch of discarded locomotives, this time replaced by diesel MAUD from Oxfordshire Ironstone. 14th August 1969. Right to left – MW 1795, HL 3780, K 5478. Workshops in the background.   S.A. Leleux

Irchester Quarries.   Woolaston pit had nothing like the depth of overburden that was so prominent a feature of Lodge pit. Here we see MAUD with a loaded train about to leave on 23rd May 1969. A 490 R&R shovel is at the ironstone face.   G.H. Starmer

on 27th June, with men kept on for dismantling and restoration work until the complete shutdown on the last Friday in September, by which time it was expected to have completed the major part of the work.

By September 1st the track had been lifted from the quarry to the water tank near the quarry entrance, and most sidings had gone, including that to the loco. shed. MAUD was used on the work, also the trackslewer to haul rail to a stacking ground by the Woolaston road for cutting up. The locomotive stock at the closure comprised 9.7.No. 17, No. 14, HOLWELL No. 30 and CARMARTHEN, all grouped in the workshops area; and MAUD, kept inside when not at work. There were still a few 'Ship Canal' wagons, including two reasonably complete, and eight 'Gloucester' wagons; and two 2 ft (?) gauge V-side tipper bodies of unknown origin.

Railway preservation was well established of course, and No. 14 went to Quainton Road; several people expressed interest in HOLWELL No. 30, too, but nothing came of it and she went with three others to Cohens for scrap. The remaining locomotive was given to Irchester Parish Council, following a request by Councillor Revd. Graham Wood, a railway enthusiast who persuaded the council to buy the locomotive from the quarry company to put in the recreation ground. However, as Mr Carden said "We have disturbed the villagers by quarrying operations for almost a century; it is about time we gave them something". So 9 was repainted by three employees (F. Inwood, F. Wood, and J.W. Rawley) in green, black and red – and looking much better than most of the locomotives when they were at work!

The smallest steam digger – the 6-ton Ruston – was acquired for private preservation, and the company tried to get some wagons preserved. A 'Ship Canal' wagon was kept and was indeed purchased by a private individual and moved to Kettering Ironworks site in November 1969; and three 'Gloucesters' – 35 complete, Nos. 11 and 17 partly dismantled – were here until the Spring of 1970. A fund was started to save 35 but proved abortive. In March 1970 there was still track in from BR to about 100 yards below the workshops, which contained a tractor, possibly hired to assist with the final stages of dismantling, as the diesel locomotive had left in January. So too had Mr Carden, disillusioned perhaps by the way things had turned out after his valiant efforts to keep the place open. He was said to 'have left the industry' at any rate; yet his innate love for it could only have been dormant, for when the opportunity for revival came at Harlaxton in 1976, he took charge of developments there with his old enthusiasm.

Irchester Quarries. MAUD pushes a train of loaded tipplers into the BR sidings for collection, 18th June 1969. Wellingborough London Road station in background, right. The grassgrown state of the track will be noted.

Ian L. Wright

Irchester Quarries. The approach to the BR line in 1969, showing signal and the Wellingborough Midland Junction signal box.   Ian L. Wright

Irchester did not go quite the same way as other quarries in Northamptonshire, however. Following negotiations commenced late in 1970, about 200 acres of the site – in effect most of the land between Rushden Road and Gipsy Lane then occupied by BSC – was purchased in April 1971 from the latter by Northamptonshire County Council as a Country Park, and formally opened on Tuesday 20th July 1971 by the Chairman of the County Council, Mrs. D.P. Oxenham, C.B.E.

The remains outside the Park will diminish with time, while those within have in general been left unaltered in essentials. The workshops were demolished, though the office and wooden shed were left, and the yard was levelled; this is close to the Park administrative office. The locomotive shed was demolished too, but leaving the concrete floor and even the pathway that led from the rear of the building up the bank to the tramway. The course of the latter is now partly incorporated in a walk from the vicinity of the calcine banks, past the shed and then towards Rushden Road, in deepening cutting as it runs past the shed site. A short section of the course of narrow gauge line towards Woolaston can be seen, leaving the standard gauge route just west of the loco. shed site, and up a gentle incline, but is then lost in a thicket. At one time the imprint of sleepers could be made out. The area hereabouts was crisscrossed by paths used by quarrymen homeward bound, and in 1968 could be seen three narrow gauge sleepers, one with a spike and metal plate in situ. With the cessation of quarrying these footpaths rapidly became overgrown, other remains disappearing with them. There were also pieces of narrow gauge rail used as lintels above the loco. shed door and one window – all gone now, of course.

Access to the locomotive shed area is easily made from a footpath at the end of Newtown Road; when the tramway was working, it was a favourite entrance for locomotive enthusiasts. New houses at the start of Newtown Road are in 'Butlin's Court', a pleasant revival of name. On Rushden Road, now incorporated into the A 45 the bridge, of red brick with a row of blue bricks along the top, survived until the doubling of the road here in 1980. However, the cutting remains – a few yards only – on the north side, with plenty of ash where the engines used to wait for the signal to be cleared for access to the main line sidings; the cutting towards the loco. shed was heavily overgrown but early in 1985 this was cleared of rubbish, landscaped and planted with trees and shrubs as part of the Park, this work being undertaken as a Manpower Services Commission project. This exposed the remains of the weighbridge, but as the route is a dead end, it is little used. Just beyond the bridge, to the east, is another heavily overgrown cutting, presumably the final gullet of the King Pit. The quarry area beyond Poplar Barn is marked by hill-and-dale formation planted over with pines and larch, but about 200 yards further to the east we come to a grove of aspens, a great deal more pleasing to the eye, and the ground is flat here; very likely this was a limestone quarry site. The southeastern perimeter is marked by the deep final gullet of Wembley pit, an impressive remnant of the former quarry workings. The central area of the Park at the eastern end is almost wholly hill-and-dale with the familiar conifer plantations, now threaded by a Nature Trail.

Considerable remains of the calcine banks are still present (1985), with ore exposed on the south side; nearby, where the banks had been cleared, the ground is covered with slack. On the other side of these lines the cutting north of Gipsy Lane, which though not filled in, had been used near the road end as an unofficial dumping ground, in reality an eyesore; further away from the road it is clear, and crossed by a small wooden footbridge to a children's play area. The cutting south of Gipsy Lane was partly filled in in the autumn of 1974 but the course of the line towards London Road can be made out. Over the next ten years the gaping Lodge Pit was filled in by Northamptonshire County Council as 'Irchester Tip' and the considerable length of gullet close to Gipsy Lane was levelled by 1984. Practically the whole of this area is now pasture, crossed by wire fences in place of hedges, and with the familiar rather barren appearance of such restored land. The bridge that carried the standard gauge tramway extension to Wollaston over the stream is still in position, embanked each side and on the south side lies about 200 yards of overgrown trackbed; beyond this starts the long terminal face of Woolaston pit, which was being filled in during 1985. It seems possible, however, that the section by the bridge might escape this treatment. Across London Road, north of the stream, there is a small sunken area that is thought to have been a Butlins working.

There are also remains to be seen of the almost forgotten and not very successful quarries in the vicinity of Chester House, north of Rushden Road. A public footpath leaves the A45 opposite the junction with Chester Road, and if we follow this for 150 yards we come to the dip due to the excavations of the Cherry Orchard Pit and to the right (north east) can be seen the terminal face by the next hedge. The tramway route can be followed in shallow cutting to the Chester House avenue and beyond on a low embankment towards Roman Town; at one time, it was said,[3] the

Irchester Quarries. Nordberg 'trackshifter' being used to recover rail during lifting operations. 24th August 1969.   S.A. Leleux

Irchester Quarries. A public footpath crossed the quarry site from Newtown Road, Little Irchester, making the ideal route for a visit to the engine shed. The quarries are closed, the tramways lifted, but the trackbed remains in the country park. This view was taken from the point where the footpath tops the embankment. Route to the quarries in centre; site of loco. shed to the left of this, in centre of picture; former narrow gauge route was to the right. Footpath continues at far left. 20th March 1979.   Eric Tonks

imprint of sleepers were still visible here, but this is not now the case, and the cut in the east rampart of the Roman Town is not very clear – but the one on the west side is very clear indeed, with a gap in the belt of trees. Beyond this point the line went across fields to the LNWR station, but the ground has been so thoroughly restored to agriculture as to leave no traces, nor are there any of the branch to the so-called 'Roman Town Quarry' lying by the A 45, though the quarry itself has left obvious traces. It should perhaps be mentioned that the Roman remains are not protected by the Department of the Environment and are not signposted. They have been examined by archaeologists from time to time and two accounts can be mentioned as they give specific references to the ironstone workings, with plans. These are (i) the very detailed *'Royal Commission on Historical Monuments; an Inventory of Archaeological Sites in Central Northamptonshire'*, with detailed plans of the Roman Town site (pp 90–96); and (ii) 'Excavations at Irchester 1962–63' by D.N. Hill and N. Anderson in *Archaeological Journal*, May 1968, with a reconstruction of the tramway route.

Various momentoes are in private hands – one enthusiast had the entrance notice board, the office rubber stamp (Irchester Ironstone Co Ltd) a builder's plate from a 'Gloucester' wagon, and a photograph that graced the office wall for many years, depicting a scene in the 1930's with a steam navvy and a locomotive.

We must be thankful for the foresight of Northamptonshire County Council in saving so much of the area for us to wander round at our leisure; yet one cannot do so without some pangs of regret at missed opportunities – which, we hasten to add, were no fault of the N.C.C. Only one of the wagons was saved in spite of opportunities freely given, and only one of the large fleet of steam quarry equipment, so prominent a feature of Irchester; we understand that there were plans to save a 15-ton Ruston navvy but they proved fruitless. Locomotives fared better; the Barclay was put on the local recreation ground, but suffered from the inevitable vandalism and, because of the 'toxic asbestos' scare, was (ineffectually) fenced off in 1978. She was moved to Wicksteed Park, Kettering, in June 1979, where she could be better cared for and kept under surveillance. The Manning Wardle that was sent to Quainton has been purchased by the Northamptonshire Ironstone Railway Trust and moved in October 1977 to Hunsbury Hill. The Trust also purchased the 'Ship Canal' wagon, which had been sold by the original purchaser to the Kettering, Corby & District Industrial Archaeology Group in 1971, and she was moved to Hunsbury Hill 28th June 1980. Attempts (fortunately unsuccessful) had been made to burn her at Kettering.

Saddest, perhaps, is the loss of those features peculiar to Irchester – the workshops (what a museum they would have made!) and the tramway relics and remains. The 'Wembley' gullet is a permanent memorial to the quarrymen, but is now becoming obscured by tall trees in parts. Irchester in its heyday was never, in our opinion, a cheerfully inviting place in the scenic sense, but was always a bit grubby and workaday, in contrast say to Scaldwell and Cranford; and this atmosphere is caught up today in the sombre pines on the hill-and-dale. But it makes one think – which is something to be thankful for.

Finally, the translation in 1987 of the headquarters of the Irchester Narrow Gauge Railway Trust from the old goods shed at Irchester station site to the brand-new building in the country park has enabled visitors to see one of the metre-gauge locomotives from the neighbouring Wellingborough quarries, superbly restored to working order. Two more former ironstone locomotives are undergoing restoration – a second one from Wellingborough and the French locomotive CAMBRAI from Loddington and Waltham quarries.

Footnotes

1. *Journal of Roman Studies*, 16, p 223. 1926.
2. 'Woolaston-portrait of a village'. David Hall. *The Woolaston Society*, 1977.
3. *Royal Commission on Historical Monuments*; letter 12th March 1985.

Grid References

Narrow gauge tramway (Butlins)

903665	Tipping dock to LNWR
904665	Level crossing of Rushden Road
904650	Locomotive shed
904660	Junction of lines to Woolaston and Irchester
906652	Woolaston terminus

Standard gauge tramway (Pain – Irchester Ironstone – South Durham)

904666	Junction with LNWR
904665	Bridge under Rushden Road
905661	Locomotive shed
909660	Workshops
911660	Reversing point near workshops

911604	Poplar Barn
907657	Gipsy Lane bridge
912658	Wembley Pit (west end)
908659	Calcine clamps by loco shed
907651	Calcine clamps by London Road
910638	Woolaston Pit terminus
914665	Roman Town Quarry
916667	Cutting through west rampart of Roman Town
919667	Embankment by Chester House
920668	Cutting by Chester House

Locomotives

First Period, c 1874–1903 (Butlin Bevan & Co Ltd)

Gauge: 3ft 8¼ins.

JONATHAN	0-4-OST	OC	HCR	145	1874	8 x 15ins	2ft 0in	New 5/1874	s/s
SOLOMON	0-4-OST	OC	HCR	156	1875	8 x 15ins	2ft 0ins	New 1/1875	s/s
SAMSON	0-4-OST	OC	HCR	185	1876	7½ x 12ins	2 ft 0½ins	New 9/1876	s/s
DELILAH	0-4-OST	OC	HCR	186	1876	7½ x 12ins	2ft 0½ins	New 9/1876	s/s

It is not certain that all these locomotives worked at Irchester (see text).

Second Period, 1912–1969 (James Pain Ltd and later owners)

Gauge: 4ft 8½ins

DAISY	0-4-OST	OC	HC	535	1900	10 x 16ins	2ft 9ins	(a)		s/s
ROTHWELL	0-4-OST	OC	P	1258	1912	12 x 16ins	3ft 0½ins	(b)		(1)
11	0-4-OST	OC	AB	1047	1905	14 x 22ins	3ft 5ins	(c)		(2)
ANCOATS	0-4-OVBT	VCG	MW	1091	1888	12 x 18ins	3ft 0ins	(d)		(3)
	Reb. Blackwell									
COCKSPUR	0-4-OST	OC	P	1289	1912	15 x 21ins	2ft 7ins	(e)		(4)
No. 1	0-4-OST	OC	HL	2412	1899	14 x 20ins	3ft 6ins	(f)		(5)
PROGRESS	0-6-OST	OC	P	1402	1912	14 x 20ins	3ft 7ins	(g)		(1)
15	0-4-OST	OC	HL	3892	1936	16 x 24ins	3ft 8ins	New 10/1936		(1)
16	0-4-OST	OC	CF	1195	1900	13 x 19ins	3ft 4ins	(h)	Scr 6/1963	
No. 17	0-4-OST	OC	HL	3946	1937	16 x 24ins	3ft 8ins	New 12/1937		(6)
19	0-4-OST	OC	AB	2101	1940	16 x 24ins	3ft 7ins	New 6/1940		(7)
ENTERPRISE	0-4-OST	OC	WB	1739	1907	14 x 20ins	3ft 6½ins	(i)		(8)
No. 9	0-6-OST	OC	AE	1787	1917	14½ x 20ins	3ft 3ins	(j)		(9)
No. 6	0-6-OST	OC	AB	1497	1916	14 x 22ins	3ft 7ins	(k)		(10)
No. 14	0-4-OST	OC	MW	1795	1912	14 x 20ins	3ft 6ins	(l)		(11)
	Reb. Ridley Shaw 1936									
MAJOR	0-4-OST	OC	AB	1363	1914	16 x 24ins	3ft 7ins	(m)		(1)
No. 8 1918	0-4-OST	OC	AB	1609	1918	16 x 22ins	3ft 7ins	(n)		(1)

HOLWELL No. 30									
	0-4-OST	OC	HL	3780	1932	16 x 24ins	2ft 10ins	(o)	(10)

9 (form.6)	0-4-0ST	OC	AB	2323	1952	16 x 24ins	3ft 7ins	(p)	(12)
7	0-4-0ST	OC	AB	2324	1952	16 x 24ins	3ft 7ins	(q)	(6)
No. 2. 50.CARMARTHEN									
	0-6-0ST	IC	K	5478	1936	16 x 22ins	3ft 6ins	(r)	(6)
MAUD	0-4-0DH		S	10142	1962	311hp	30 ton	(s)	(13)

(a)   ex Corby Quarries (James Pain), 1912
(b)   ex Glendon East Quarries
(c)   ex Cargo Fleet Ironworks, Yorkshire NR,1922
(d)   ex Blackwell, Northampton, c 1922; form. Stanley Bros Ltd, Stockingford, Warwickshire.
(e)   ex Morris & Shaw Ltd, Birch Coppice Colliery, Warwickshire, 1924
(f)   ex Cargo Fleet Iron Co Ltd, Woodland Colliery, c 1926
(g)   ex Desborough (Co-op) Quarries, via Blackwell, Northampton c1927
(h)   ex W.Whitwell & Co Ltd, Thornaby, 1937
(i)   ex Storefield Quarries 6/1944; to Storefield 1/1945; ex Storefield 1948
(j)   ex South Durham Steel & Iron Co Ltd, Stockton, c 1952
(k)   ex Malleable Works, Stockton, 8/1953
(l)   ex Wensley Lime Co Ltd 3/1957
(m)   ex SDSI, West Hartlepool 11/1957
(n)   ex SDSI, West Hartlepool, 2/1959
(o)   ex Stanton & Staveley Ltd, Holwell Works, Leicestershire 8/1963
(p)   ex Cargo Fleet Ironworks, 4/1964
(q)   ex Cargo Fleet Ironworks, 7/1964
(r)   ex Stewarts & Lloyds Minerals Ltd, Glendon East Quarries 8/1968
(s)   ex Stewarts & Lloyds Minerals Ltd, Market Overton Quarries 2/1969

(1)   to George Cohen Sons & Co Ltd, Cransley depot, for scrap 12/1966
(2)   to Cochrane & Co Ltd, Desborough Quarries c 1925; ex Desborough c 1927. To Storefield Quarries 1949
(3)   to United Steel Cos Ltd, Irthlingborough Ironworks, c 1923
(4)   to Storefield Quarries c 1940; ex Storefield 4/1942; to Storefield 3/1943
(5)   to Storefield Quarries 4/1942; ex Storefield 1947; to Wensley Lime Co Ltd, Yorkshire, 1949
(6)   to Cohen, Cransley for scrap 9/1969
(7)   to Storefield Quarries 3/1942
(8)   to Storefield Quarries 1951; ex Storefield 3/1960; to Storefield 11/1965
(9)   Scrapped by T.H. Sheppard & Sons Ltd, Wellingborough 8/1967
(10)   to Storefield Quarries 8/1954; ex Storefield 4/1962. to Cohen, Cransley, for scrap 9/1969
(11)   to London Railway Preservation Society, Quainton Road, 8/1969
(12)   to Irchester Parish Council, Woolaston Road recreation ground 8/1969
(13)   to Stewarts & Lloyds Minerals Ltd, Glendon East Quarries 1/1970

Quarry Machines

12 ton	S. Navvy	Wh					Scr c 1920's	
No. 20	S. Navvy	RP	446	1916	2¼ Cu.Yds.	31 ft.	New 5/1916	(1)
No. 5	S. Transporter	RP	459 or 460	1916			New 8/1916	Scr c. 1920's

No. 20	S. Navvy	RH	730	1920	2¼ Cu.Yds. 31 ft.	New 10/1922	(2)
No. 15	S. Navvy	RH	779	1923		New 3/1923	Scr c. 1970
No. 20	S. Navvy. Long Jib	RH	814	1924		New 5/1924	(3)
No. 20	S. Navvy	RH	509	1918	2¼ Cu.Yds. 31 ft.	(a)	s/s
No. 5	SND Transporter	RH	582	1920		(a)	s/s
No. 10	S. Navvy	RH	778	1923	1½ Cu.Yds.	(b)	(4)
No. 20	S. Navvy	RH	513	1918	2¼ Cu.Yds. 31 ft.	(c)	(5)
No. 12	S. Navvy	RH	525	1918	2 Cu.Yds	(d)	(6)
No. 6	S. Dragline	RH	887	1924		(e)	(7)
No. 300	S. Shovel	RH	1643	1930	5½ Cu.Yds. 95 ft.	New 6/1930	(8)
43RB	E. Dragline	RB	2460	1934		New 5/1934	(9)
480	E. Shovel	R&R	254	1935		New 5/1935	(10)
5360	E. Stripping Shovel	R&R	440	1936	8 Cu.Yds. 104 ft.	New 5/1936	(11)
480	E. Shovel	R&R	446	1936		New 5/1936	s/s 1969
55RB	E. Dragline	RB	4615	1939		New 11/1939	(12)
490	E. Shovel	R&R	2490	1951		New 6/1951*	s/s
43RB	D. Shovel	RB	17537	1954		New 3/1954*	(13)
43RB	D. Shovel	RB	18364	1954		New 9/1954*	(14)
5W	E. Walking Dragline	RB	19343	1955		New 4/1955	(15)

* Believed to be New to Irchester.

(a)   ex Twywell Quarries c 1924
(b)   ex Twywell Quarries 9/1924
(c)   ex Desborough Quarries c 1927
(d)   ex Desborough Quarries 1927
(e)   ex Henry Boot & Sons, contractors.

(1)   New to King pit. To Wembley pit. Scr.
(2)   at King pit (?). s/s
(3)   New to Wembley pit. s/s
(4)   at Roman Town, pit 1927. To Storefield Quarries 1942
(5)   at Wembley pit. s/s
(6)   at Cherry Orchard pit; to calcine bank. to Storefield Quarries c 1940
(7)   to Storefield Quarries c 1940; returned. to Hollins Hall for preservation
(8)   New to Wembley pit. To Storefield Quarries c 1944
(9)   To Storefield Quarries c 1943; returned c 1944; to Twywell Quarries in late 1960s
(10)   To Storefield Quarries, as crane c. 1944
(11)   New to Lodge pit. Scr c 1968
(12)   to British Industrial Sand Ltd, 1970
(13)   to Corby Quarries c 1969
(14)   to Pitsford Quarries
(15)   to Corby Quarries (Wakerley) c 1970

Irchester Quarries. The country park has retained many traces of the former quarry tramway system; seen here is the trackbed looking towards Gipsy Lane from the workshop area; the footbridge (put in by the park authorities) leads to the calcine clamp area. 19th October 1985. A.J. Cocklin

Irchester Quarries. North of Rushden Road lay the isolated Roman Town and Cherry Orchard quarries, served by a separate branch tramway from Wellingborough station yard. Between Roman Town and Chester House the trackbed was slightly embanked above the fields, and is now used as a farm track – as shown here, 19th October 1985. The lime tree avenue at the rear lines the drive to Chester House. A.J. Cocklin

IRCHESTER QUARRIES

Owners: Stanton Ironworks Co Ltd.

Quarrying north of the Wellingborough–Higham Ferrers road took place in three short-lived stages; by Butlin Bevan in the 1870s, by Irchester Ironstone in the late 1920s, and by Stanton at the present site half way between the other two. The area was separated from the others by the Midland Railway main line and was itself further subdivided by the Higham Ferrers branch, the only portion completed of a proposed line from Irchester Junction to Raunds, authorized on 25th July 1890. It seems that construction of the line revealed the presence of ironstone at the junction, and a lease was obtained by Stanton from the Knuston Hall estate (Arkwright family) in 1892, and comprised about 50 acres, not all containing ironstone, on the southern slope of the Nene valley and extending from the MR main line as far as Ditchford Road. The brief mention in Hewlett and a plan in BSC archives were our only sources of information until John McCrickard turned up some interesting details recorded in the MR 'Weekly Operating Notices' preserved in the National Railway Museum York, and kindly passed on by Geoffrey Webb in a letter of 20th July 1985.

The branch was opened for passenger traffic on 1st September 1893, but two months earlier, on Monday 3rd July 1893, the 300-yard section from the junction to the first overbridge was opened for goods and mineral traffic, of sufficient importance to justify the opening of Irchester Junction signal box on that day; the traffic, without any doubt, was ironstone for Stanton, for which Stanton Siding was laid on the north side of the line, and the quarries evidently started production in July 1893. Working on the north side was limited, as the ground sloped towards the Nene, and operations were transferred to the south side of the branch; and on Sunday, 22nd January 1899 the running line and siding exchanged places, resulting in a tighter curve for the former. This might not be unique, but it is certainly a rare railway manoeuvre.

Whether a tramway feeder was used is not known with certainty; Stanton normally used tramways in quarries, even small ones, but carts were probably used here as the distance to the furthest working face was only a few hundred yards, and no tramway appears on the 1900 25ins OS. An unusual feature was that the quarry actually encroached on the railway bank, and ore from the railway side of the fence had to be separately weighed for the calculation of royalties.

Operations on the south side were more extensive than on the north, but were still quite small by general standards and work ceased in November 1908, according to Hewlett. The visible remains are almost nil, not surprisingly, as they were shallow outcrop workings; for the same reason the quarries did not even qualify for mention in LQ.

Grid References

923673   Quarry site north of Irchester Junction

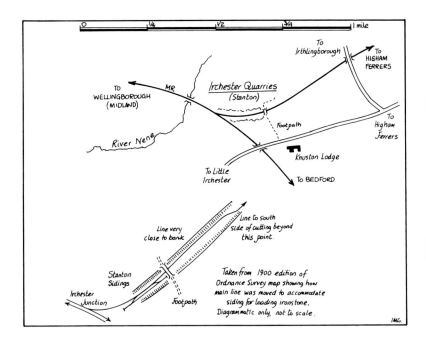

STANTONGATE QUARRIES

Owners; Stanton Ironworks Co Ltd AND Thomas Butlin & Co Ltd

In 1874 the Stanton Ironworks Co Ltd obtained leases of the stone under land west of the Midland Railway and north of Wellingborough, owned by Major Vivian and the Ecclesiastical Commissioners, together with wayleaves from Lord Overstone, a prominent landowner who had much to do with local railway history; and to serve this area a standard gauge line was built from the Midland Railway, closely following the course of the later line through Wellingborough Ironworks. The Stantongate quarries themselves lay east and west of the Wellingborough–Kettering road, and a narrow gauge tramway was laid from them via a level crossing north of Vicarage Farm House to a tipping dock at the terminus of the standard gauge line, traffic commencing in 1875. The 1883 OS map shows also a separate line east of the road and terminating thereat, about 150 yards south of the level crossing; the ownership of this line is unknown. Also, according to BSC sources, Butlin's quarried ground on the west side of the main road a quarter mile northwest of Vicarage Farm on each side of the track to Waterworks Farm. We have no knowledge of a tramway here but there may well have been one to a roadside tipping dock.

T. Butlin & Co Ltd had been quarrying the area north of Wellingborough in the 1850's, as we have seen, gradually moving northwards to the vicinity of Breeze Hill Farm and westwards towards the road by Vicarage Farm; and by an agreement of 1888 with the Stanton company, they laid a narrow gauge tramway to a tipping dock alongside a branch siding near the terminus of the standard gauge line. Stanton placed Butlin's output on rail for conveyance to the MR.

The Stantongate lease expired in 1895 and the whole system seems to have been lifted very soon afterwards – at any rate it does not appear on the 1899 OS. Details of motive power are not recorded but an old farm hand stated that the 'main line' was cable-operated, though this seems a tall order for a standard gauge line of that date; possibly steam locomotives were employed – though there is not the slightest evidence of any. The narrow gauge may have been worked by horses or by cable.

Grid References

885693	Terminus of line by main road
889694	Tipping dock to s.g line
885693	Tipping dock to road
883691	Terminus of line west of road

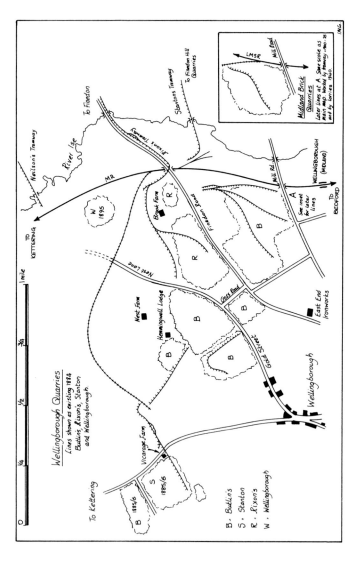

MIDLAND BRICK QUARRIES

Owners: Midland Brick Co (Wellingborough) Ltd; Wellingborough Iron Co Ltd from 29th September 1937.

These quarries are described in GSM as lying east of Wellingborough, west of the railway and south of Wellingborough Ironworks, and are therefore a continuation of the area once quarried by Thomas Butlin to supply his East End Works. The business of the proprietors was making bricks, but the ironstone and clay are close in this district, as we have noted at several quarries (Cogenhoe, Irthlingborough, etc); and Midland Brick are recorded in LQ as producing ironstone over quite a long period, 1901 to 1925, though it was probably intermittent rather than regular.

The quarry was a redevelopment of the area between Eastfield Road and the Midland Railway, worked in the 1880's by Butlins, who used a standard gauge tramway. In Butlin's day there was another branch as far as what is now Cannon Street, over an area long since built up. The Midland Brick quarry was on a much smaller scale and was served by a simple 2ft gauge line, down to a tipping dock at (or over) a MR siding. According to Jack Roberts, who saw the line at work in September 1924, it was hand operated. The ore was dug by hand and sold, some of it going to Wellingborough furnaces, but some as far away as Middlesbrough.

The area of unworked stone – about 2½ acres – was leased by Mr R.H. Whitworth of the brick company for seven years from 29th September 1937 to Wellingborough Iron Co Ltd. The latter brought in a 21RB diesel dragline to open up the quarry, where operations appear to have commenced early in 1940, in which year NSI records output removed by lorry – a point worth emphasising. A few very early and small pits used horse and cart transport but at Midland Brick was the first known instance of the use of motor vehicles, an example copied extensively in later years, particularly north of the Welland. But their usage was shortlived; even at the low royalty of 3¼d per ton, the stone proved not worth extracting, and the lease was terminated in the same year. Subsequent building has erased most of the quarry site, and even near the BR line no traces are visible; but the tiny pit has its niche in ironstone history.

Grid References

As these areas are almost completely built over, grid references are of little consequence.

904688	Tipping Dock
902686	Terminus of tramway

Quarry Machine

21RB	D. Dragline		RB	2511	1934	¾ Cu.Yds.	40 ft.	(a)	(1)

(a) ex South Witham Limestone Quarries c 1939

(1) returned to South Witham 1940

THE FINEDON GROUP

Contemporaneously with the rapid development east and south of Wellingborough in mid-Victorian times, even more intensive activity was under way to the north. Apart from the 'Stantongate' area on the west, these developments were centred on Finedon, to the east. The Glendon Iron Co's Finedon Furnaces, alongside the Midland Railway main line, started production in 1866 and lasted 25 years, but the quarries continued in other hands up to 1946. These were all on the northwest side of Finedon, while on the southwest Rixon & Co started quarrying in 1874, and in 1886 had their own Wellingborough Furnaces just north of the town. The Stanton Ironworks Co Ltd also started quarrying in the vicinity – at Finedon Hill in 1875 – and eventually took over the furnaces and quarries of Wellingborough Iron Co Ltd, as Rixon's enterprise had become. The quarries outlasted the ironworks by a few years to close in 1966. There were two other operators; Neilson, a Scottish entrepreneur, entered the Finedon district in 1880, and Keeble & Jellett at Finedon Park in 1913. Neilson's sites were acquired by Wellingborough Iron Co Ltd, and Keeble & Jellett's by Ebbw Vale Steel, Iron & Coal Co Ltd. The intensive nature of the extraction round Finedon led to the introduction of mining by Neilson and Stanton, which was greatly extended by Wellingborough until machines were developed capable of dealing with the same deposits by opencast methods.

FINEDON HILL QUARRIES AND MINES

Owners: Stanton Ironworks Co Ltd.

This system represents Stanton's first entry into the Wellingborough area, where they were later to play so significant a part. The lease from William Mackworth Dolben of Finedon Hall for working stone in the vicinity of Finedon Hill Farm was dated 1st January 1869 but output did not commence until 1875, when a lease was obtained from Mr H.M.

Stockdale, for 30 years from 29th September 1874, for land southeast of Finedon Road bridge to gain access to the Midland Railway, so possibly there was some delay there. The first workings were east of the farm buildings and were connected by a tramway of (it is believed) 2ft 6ins gauge to an elevated tipping dock adjacent to the Midland Railway at Finedon Road bridge. At this time the line was worked by horse traction. By 1884 the track had reached Sidegate Lane and in the same year the lease was extended to include two fields north of this lane, between Carrol Spring Farm and Finedon Road. In 1890 the lease was further extended and by 1899 quarries northwest of Finedon Hill Farm were being worked, and a bridge under Sidegate Lane was made to reach the ground beyond. On this tramway cable haulage by a steam engine at the railway end was introduced; the date is not known but the geography of the system suggests that it coincided with the extension beyond Sidegate Lane. After leaving the MR, the existing line turned east by north then ran straight as far as a point a quarter mile northwest of South Hill Farm, and from this point another straight, single inclined line was laid to the working area; loaded tubs were lowered down the incline by a rope passing round a fixed pulley at the top, then a set of empties were pulled up by the hauling engine. The tubs were 5ft x 4ft x 2ft, holding 40 cubic feet (25–30 cwt of ore). For the detailed information on this novel method of operating we are indebted to the diary (in the records of the Burghley Estate Office) of W.J. Hudson, Manager of Easton on the Hill quarries, who visited the Wellingborough area on 20th May 1903 to get information on the operating of such inclines. He gives the hauling engine as being 'at the foot of the incline' but its position at the railway end, as quoted by Hewlett, is confirmed by local memory.

At the tipping dock a steam-operated hoist was employed to raise the tubs for tipping their contents into standard gauge wagons alongside. Tracks to the quarry face continued to be worked by horses. The steam hauling engine had seen many years' service at Dale Colliery, near Ilkeston, and came from there after the colliery had closed; Ted Barber (whom we shall meet under the Leicestershire headings) who had operated the engine at Dale, was sent to Wellingborough to take charge of it at its new site, where it displaced six horses, as recorded in *'The Stantonian'* for September 1946, p 13. At some time the tipping arrangement at the MR end was modified, though probably the hauling arrangements were unchanged. The 1884 and 1901 OS maps show a tipping stage parallel to the MR siding; the 1924 OS shows the stage a

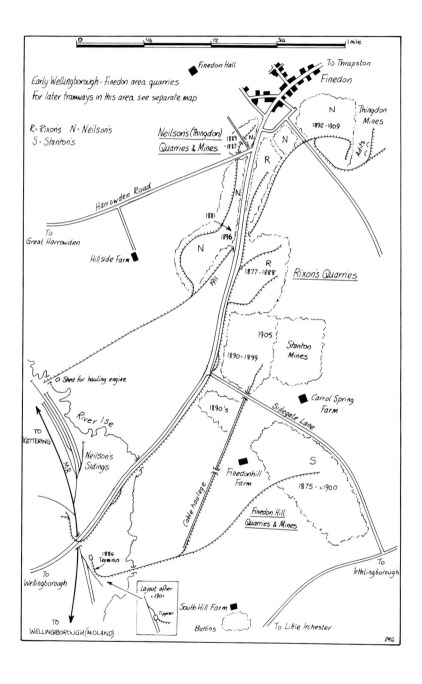

little further west, **over** the MR siding, with the tramway lines running up to it and down from it. The embankment for this was made of furnace slag dust.

By 1909 all the stone under shallow cover had been removed and in that year the underground Finedon Hill mine was opened; this was simply an adit with an 8ft heading driven into the hillside in direct line with the incline, and into which the tubs were taken by pony for loading (see *Kettering Guardian*, 15th July 1910). The tramway extension was taken beneath the Wellingborough Iron Co's metre line by a wooden bridge. The mine was worked by the pillar and stall method, up to 7ft of stone being taken, leaving some ironstone in the roof, but this was removed as far as possible on retreat; as a result the surface of the area became derelict owing to irregular subsidence. The area to be dealt with was quite small – only two fields – and according to Mr L.J. Dunkley, a driver, there were only two ponies. Work continued at the mine until the expiry of the lease in 1918 when, according to Hewlett, the plant was sold to Wellingborough Iron Co Ltd. The tramway system was taken over by a new company, Southhill Ironstone Mines Ltd, who opened up a quarry to the north of South Hill Farm, as described in the next section.

The course of the lower part of the tramway as far as the Ise is traceable but overgrown between its hedges, but the tipping dock – the crumbling bank of which was in position in the 1950's – has now disappeared. The fields below road level south of Sidegate Lane indicate former quarrying areas; the inclined section of the tramway has disappeared under the plough but the position of the bridge under Sidegate Lane is revealed by a red brick parapet on the north side only, the bridge being filled beneath. The mining area has been obliterated by the later operations of Wellingborough Iron Co Ltd.

Grid References

905692	Tipping dock to MR
915700	Sidegate Lane bridge
910691	Top of incline
917704	Adit

SOUTH HILL FARM QUARRIES

Owners: Southhill Ironstone Mines Ltd

This small and shortlived concern is only mentioned as such in NSI and its predecessor GSM: LQ is silent, the quarries being too shallow to require the attention of H.M. Inspector of Quarries, while *Rylands Directory* lists workings at South Hill by J. Clarke of Rushden for 1920–24. The quarries were connected by tramway to Stanton's closed Finedon Hill line, leading to fruitless searching among Stanton records for information; and it is surprising that Hewlett makes no mention whatever of this venture, of which he must have been aware. It was as recently as October 1986 that specific details came to light in BSC archives, thanks to the efforts of Norman Bellamy of the Regional Property Department, and we take up the story from this source.

South Hill Farm lies to the south of Finedon Hill Farm, and John Clark (without the 'e'), described as an 'Ironstone Merchant and Shoe Manufacturer', leased the minerals in and under the farm for the term of 21 years from 29th September 1912. The obvious access to the Midland Railway was via Stanton's Finedon Hill tramway, and Clark initially made arrangements with Stanton to convey his output. This however was not put into effect; instead, Clark obtained a wayleave for 14 years from 25th December 1912 from the Wellingborough Iron Co Ltd (the owners of Finedon Hill Farm) to lay a tramway, to be fenced both sides, connecting with Stanton's line, Stanton giving permission for the use of the lower portion of the latter as soon as they had ceased their operations at Finedon Hill mines by expiry or determination of the lease.

The quarries lay on the northwest side of South Hill Farm (Butlin Bevan had quarried on the south side some years before) and the tramway was laid to connect with Stanton's 2ft 6ins (believed) system at the foot of the inclined section. A locomotive was introduced, provision for such having been made in an addendum to the indenture of 2nd April 1913 (embodying the wayleave and associated matters) in the form of a safeguard to the lessors from possible damage by sparks. Another addendum authorised the purchase of Stanton's tipping plant at the MR sidings.

Concerning the locomotive, Frank Frost of Wellingborough Iron Co Ltd remembers riding on it as a lad, and Len Dunkley of Finedon remembers seeing the engine, which he describes thus – "I feel sure it was of the type used by Barlows of Burton Latimer", with which Frank concurs. If indeed it was a Bagnall as implied, a ready candidate was available in the ironstone industry in WB 1554 of Wakerley quarries, displaced there by their new Bagnall of 1919; Bert Smith, who was born at Wakerley, remembers seeing only one locomotive there, so it seems pretty certain that the new one displaced the old. Perhaps we had better not speculate further. Frank states that the locomotive was housed in a shed of wood and corrugated iron close to the junction with Stanton's tramway. Len Dunkley says the quarries were managed by 'Peg leg' Pearce, who also drove the locomotive; Fred Pearce, his father, was manager at Wellingborough Iron Co's quarries. The wagons were one-ton side-tippers, and were taken by the engine to Finedon Bridge sidings; these wagons had quite high flared sides, Frank Frost tells us.

Thus far the story, though unusual, is simple enough except for Hewlett's unaccountable silence; but, as Greg Evans learned in the winter of 1987/8 in conversation with Frank Frost and Aubrey Richardson (born 1915 in Midland Cottages overlooking the MR), the situation was far more complex. In the first place, Clark had leased South Hill Farm for ironstone extraction, but at a later date must have obtained permission to work north of Sidegate Lane, reopening Stanton's cable-operated tramway to do so. Thus, at the tipping dock in the early 1920's there was the extraordinary spectacle of wagons being pushed by the locomotive from South Hill Farm, and others hauled by cable from Sidegate Lane. Both men recall seeing the latter wagons 'dotted along the rope' on their way down. At the junction with the line to South Hill Farm the cable was taken beneath the points in a brick-lined culvert to avoid fouling the locomotive and wagons, and over this section the ropeway wagons were detached from the cable, pushed over the points and reattached to the cable for the journey to the tipping dock. On the single track section the up and down cables ran on rollers with two channels, sunk between the rails. At the tipping stage the tramway divided into two to form a long loop, and ropeway wagons were hauled up by the cable, tipped to empty their contents via a steel chute into railway wagons below, and then formed into a train to return together. This was in effect the system obtaining in Stanton's day, as described by Hudson. The cable was kept running for working hours; two wires ran alongside the line and if it was necessary to stop the cable, scraping the wires together would alert the driver in the engine house close to the stage. The cable was greased by a boy wielding a long-handled stick, carried in a wooden box with a leather handle. From South Hill Farm the locomotive pushed trains of four wagons to the tipping stage and collected these for the return journey. Obviously, the outputs from South Hill and from Sidegate Lane had to be kept separate – possibly by working on different days. The ropeway wagons are presumed to have been Stanton's originals, described by Frank Frost as 'little boxes', which Aubrey Richardson thought were of iron on wooden frames, and again side-tipping.

Aubrey Richardson believes the system was closed in 1926; W.J. Redden & Sons are believed to have dismantled the ropeway for scrap. The engine house was demolished in the early 1930's and the chimney blown up. The remains of the tramway are described in the Finedon Hill section; the only specifically Southhill relic is the site of the quarry by the farm, still clearly visible as a depression in the ground to the northwest; the Butlin Bevan site is also visible to the south.

Grid References

913690	Quarry
911692	Junction of tramway with Finedon Hill tramway

Locomotive

Gauge: 2ft 6ins

0-4-OST	OC	WB	1554	1898	6 x 9ins	1ft 7ins	(a)	s/s

(a) ex Partington Steel & Iron Co Ltd, Wakerley Quarries. c.1920

The identity of this locomotive is unknown but could be as above

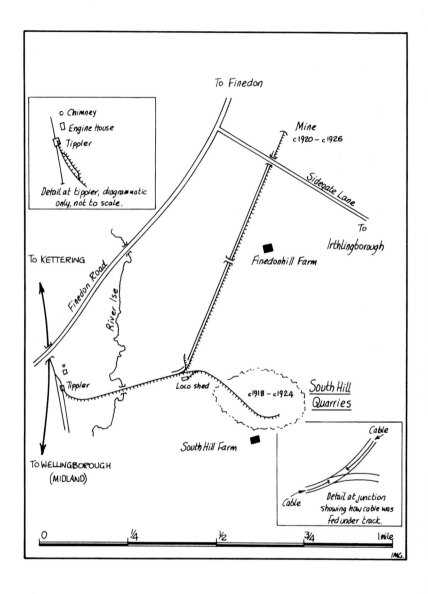

To Finedon

Mine
c1920 – c1926

Sidegate Lane

To Irthlingborough

o Chimney
☐ Engine House
☐ Tippler

Detail at tippler, diagrammatic only, not to scale.

To KETTERING

Finedon Road

River Ise

Finedonhill Farm

Tippler

Loco shed

c1918 – c1924

South Hill Quarries

South Hill Farm

To WELLINGBOROUGH (MIDLAND)

Cable

Cable

Detail at junction showing how cable was fed under track.

| 0 | ¼ | ½ | ¾ | 1 mile |

THINGDON QUARRIES AND MINES

Owners; Walter Neilson: Wellingborough Iron Co Ltd from 1911.

Walter Neilson, a Scot as his name implies, owned land at Finedon and started up in business as an iron ore proprietor in the late 19th century, becoming after James Pain probably the most important independent operator; though unlike Pain he never moved elsewhere. Hewlett gives the start of operations as 1879, but according to MS production commenced in 1882 and the first known lease is dated 25th March 1880, covering an area of just over 22 acres in the angle between Finedon Road and Harrowden Road. The lessor was Mrs Frances Mackworth Dolben of Finedon Hall, and the term 21 years; a further lease was enacted with date 25th March 1883 for a period of 18 years (i.e. to terminate concurrently with the earlier lease) for a rather smaller area north of Harrowden Road and bordering Finedon Road as far as Bell Hill, the latter area in Finedon Park itself.

To convey the ore to the Midland Railway a tramway of 2ft 4ins gauge was constructed, the upper section on land leased from Earl Fitzwilliam in 1881, the lower section possibly on land owned by Neilson; this latter section was cable-operated (see description below) but the upper portion leading to the quarries was worked by horses. This line was taken under Harrowden Road by a brick tunnel in 1883, with a further tunnel beneath the avenue leading to the Hall; the quarrying activities involved the closure of this approach to the Hall and destruction of some trees, but the area was only partially opened up, as the Harrowden Road bridge was said not to have fulfilled the conditions laid down by Irthlingborough Highways Board, and was only used for a few months (*"Wellingborough News"* 28th March 1890). On a plan in BSC archives the Finedon Park area is annotated 'idea abandoned 1887'. Quarrying was continued south of the tunnel on land close to the main road as far as the top of the rope-worked incline. The northern part of the leased area was purchased and quarried 26 years later by Keeble & Jellett as part of their Finedon Park quarries; and they also used the tunnel, from the opposite direction to Neilson.

By 1890 Neilson had nearly exhausted the area south of Harrowden Road, and transferred operations to ground on the east side of Finedon Road, by virtue of a lease from Miss Mackworth Dolben in 1891; this was reached by a tunnel under Finedon Road, bored in 1892. Originally it had been intended that the tramway should pass under the road close to the village but, following local objections, the route was diverted further south. W.J. Hudson visited the line, and that at Finedon Hill, in 1903, to obtain guidance for his Easton on the Hill system, and he describes the equipment. There was a double line of tramway some two miles long, and an endless rope ³⁄₄ ins in diameter driven by a steam engine at the lower terminus near the railway. This rope was kept running continually except at mealtimes and at night, and small 'trams' carrying about 16 cwt of ore were attached to the cable by a clip. They arrived at the tippler at about quarter-minute intervals, were detached, emptied and reattached to the return rope. The ore was tipped on to calcining heaps. Wagons are described as 'side tippers and wooden trams'. 'Neilson Sidings' on the Midland Railway were well above the level of the river Ise that runs alongside, and the tramway was described to Frank Frost (Traffic Manager of Wellingborough Iron Co Ltd) by an older man as 'continuing to rise on a long gentle slope until it got to the shed at railway height'. From an aerial photograph Greg Evans confirms that this was an embankment, though there are no present-day remains. The shed would be to house the tippler, no doubt, and the calcine heaps would be on railway level.

Neilson quarried limestone from his more easterly properties, and some ironstone between this area and the road. Opencast working continued up to 1908, when heavy overburden was encountered because of geological faults, and experimental headings were driven to test the suitability of the rock for mining; these proved successful, and mining was introduced, but according to Mr Field (of Wellingborough Iron Co Ltd) Neilson lacked expertise in mining methods and soon ceased operating. After the mines had been standing idle for about a year, the lease was acquired (in 1911) by the Wellingborough Iron Co Ltd, the southernmost of whose opencast workings at Finedon Glebe had by then reached the boundary of the Neilson lease; the new owners reopened the mine under the direction of a German mining engineer, Carl Steiner, the output continuing to travel down Neilson's tramway until 1929 (according to Gerald Farrow, who started as a miner's mate a year or so earlier), when it was diverted to Wellingborough's metre gauge line, as described under that section. The Neilson tramway was finally taken up in 1933/4.

There were extensive remains of the Neilson system until the middle 1970's, and there are still some today. The skew tunnel beneath the Wellingborough–Finedon road has parapets on both sides (very ruinous by 1978), that on the east of red brick with blue triangular capping, that on the west of red brick with a line of bricks on their sides along the top. Where the tramway emerged on the east side, the line was covered over for a triangular area (as main line skew bridges sometimes are) and a shallow cutting beyond shows the course of the line, which however disappears among allotments at ground level until the 'green lane' is reached. West of the main road bridge the traces are less obvious apart from a sunken field north of the hedge; there are practically no traces of the course of the line on to Wellingborough Sidings. Of the original route towards Harrowden Road a few traces can be seen and there is a parapet on the south side of Harrowden Road, of red brick with blue capping. North of the bridge the (sunken) area was in 1976 covered by new houses, but on the south side the lower levels due to quarrying are visible.

It is in the quarry and mining area that the greatest changes have taken place in recent years, following the case where some children penetrated one of the old adits, nearly with tragic results; as it was, they spent the night in the mines and were found next day. Up to then the remains northeast of the 'green lane' were clearly defined, with a terminal gullet of the ironstone quarry left unfilled; this became deeper at its northern end and in the very steep cliff running north-south were two adits to Thingdon mines, half hidden by earth falls. At a higher level was the course of the tramway crossing the gullet towards some limestone quarries. Boundary hedges were still in place. The very small wagon described in the Wellingborough section could well have been one of Neilson's, as described by Hudson. However, the area was completely levelled in 1976–7 and hardly any traces of these old workings now remain. At the BR end, Neilson Sidings were lifted in the Spring of 1985, but the signal box lettered 'Neilson Sidings' (sic) was still in use. Of the method of transfer from the narrow gauge nothing can be made out. The embankment that formerly brought the tramway up to railway level has been completely removed, but its course alongside the hedge is revealed in the freshly-turned soil in autumn as it is much paler in colour and heavily strewn with bricks, compared with the rest of the field. There is no sign of the bridge over the Ise.

The most lasting memorial to Neilson lies in Finedon itself, where a number of roads close to, and in some cases on, the former quarrying area, bear names of Scottish origin, e.g. Summerlee, Kenmuir Roads. The sunken ground behind the houses – in some reaching half way up the gardens – indicate the extent of quarrying.

Finedon Group

Grid References

902701	Tipping dock to MR
914709	Bridge under main road
914714	Harrowden Lane bridge
920715	Adit
923714	Limestone quarry terminus

WELLINGBOROUGH QUARRIES AND MINES

Owners: Rixon & Co.; Rixon's Iron & Brick Co Ltd from 18th June 1883; Wellingborough Iron Co Ltd from 12th February 1889; Stewarts & Lloyds Minerals Ltd from 29th October 1962.

The firm of Rixon & Co (James Rixon and William Henry Ashwell) owned a brickworks at Wellingborough on the northern side of the town, but they were quick to appreciate the value of the ironstone worked in the vicinity from the middle of the century, and in 1874 started quarrying on their own account at Finedon, east of the road to Wellingborough, on ground presumably leased from the Mackworth Dolben family. A tramway was laid alongside this road, which to this day retains its characteristic wide grass verge, crossed the Ise by a separate wooden bridge parallel to the road bridge, then crossed the road on the level at the railway bridge to end at a presumed tipping dock alongside the Stantongate line. This tramway was horse-worked and Hewlett, writing in 1934, states that "the rumbling of the wagons, the shouting and cracking of whips, the swinging lanterns after dark, are still remembered by old inhabitants".

At this time Rixon & Co quarried iron ore solely for resale but, doubtless inspired by the success of Butlin's enterprise, the proprietors decided to enter the ironmaking business themselves, and Rixon's Iron & Brick Co Ltd was formed in 1883 to take over the effects of Rixon & Co. The prospectus files in the Stock Exchange records (extracted and kindly passed on by Frank Jux) records that the plant included about 4½ miles of tramway, over 100 metre gauge ore wagons, 28 horses and the necessary stabling, and farm implements for about 160 acres of land. There were also 251 8-ton railway wagons. On land leased (and purchased in 1910) from Mr H.M. Stockdale the company erected two blast furnaces, one being put in blast in 1884 and the other in 1886. 728 acres of land in the parishes of Finedon and Burton Latimer were leased from the Ecclesiastical Commissioners for 50 years from 29th September 1883, this term being presumed, as a renewed lease for 60 years dates from 29th September 1933. Also in 1883 Rixon & Co obtained from John Spencer a 21-year lease of 'several closes' occupied by Benjamin Allen. The location of this area is not known but Hewlett states that "we have it on good authority that Rixon also worked a small area immediately south of the works", so it was probably that. On the north side of Finedon Road,

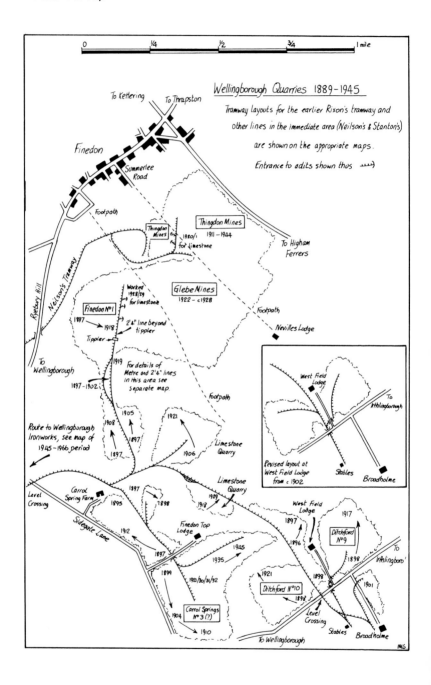

Wellingborough Quarries 1889-1945

Tramway layouts for the earlier Rixon's tramway and other lines in the immediate area (Neilson's & Stanton's) are shown on the appropriate maps.

Entrance to adits shown thus ⤵

west of Hillside Road, allotments are now on former quarried areas and the OS for the period shows a tramway between this area and the works. There was also a small quarry south of Brook Farm. It is probable that all the narrow gauge tramways associated with the ironworks were of the same gauge.

Two locomotives of 3ft 3ins gauge (nominal) were purchased from the Hunslet Engine Co but it is not certain where they worked. One would expect them to operate the mile-long tramway to Finedon quarries, but the absence of any remembrance of them suggests they did not, and possibly they worked the Hillside Road area nearer the works. However, the end of the horse tramway was soon to be accomplished, if not already done, for in 1887 Rixon's Iron & Brick Co Ltd went into liquidation and was sold on 4th August 1888 (*Wellingborough News*, 27th July 1888 – thanks to Russell Wear for this); the Wellingborough Iron Co Ltd was formed in September 1888 to take over the plant – which it did in February 1889 – work in the meantime having been carried on by the liquidator as before.

One of the first acts of the new owners was to build a completely new tramway of metre gauge to Finedon quarries; this line started from the works, where a raised platform was arranged for the wagons to discharge their contents, tunneled beneath the Midland Railway north of Finedon Road bridge, then climbed the hillside obliquely to the road, which was crossed on the level about a quarter mile from the railway bridge. This tramway crossed Sidegate Lane on the level and ran to the rear of Carrol Spring Farm; this involved crossing Side Gate Field and The Long Field that had been leased to Stanton for ironstone extraction, but a wayleave was granted to Wellingborough Iron Co by Mrs Frances Mackworth Dolben, with the consent of Stanton. The first pair of locomotives were replaced by three slightly larger Hunslets that, with a Bagnall obtained 1918, worked the traffic unaided until the system closed in 1932. The numbers of the narrow gauge locomotives dovetailed with those of the ironworks. Wagons are believed to have been wooden side-tippers. The ironworks surrounded the site of Stanton's standard gauge line to Stantongate quarries, and in 1889 an agreement was made whereby Wellingborough Iron Co Ltd was granted the use of Stanton's siding between Nest Lane and the Midland Railway, and in return undertook the haulage of ironstone trucks from the tipping docks. Thus began Stanton's close association with Wellingborough Ironworks. Working of Rixon's Finedon quarries was continued clockwise (easterly) and four quarry faces were opened up in the vicinity of Carrol Spring Farm.

In addition to the Finedon quarries, Rixon's also operated quarries at Ditchford, with a tramway connection to the LNWR east of Ditchford Station; these quarries are quoted in an LNWR working time table of November 1886[1] as closed but they were reopened by the Wellingborough Iron Co Ltd, at a date not precisely known, but certainly before 1895. Mr. Field, a foreman at Wellingborough quarries who had worked there all his life, remembered these quarries, and mentioned the stables used by Rixon's horses, a building not demolished until the 1980's. To obviate the circuitous haulage via the LNWR and MR at Wellingborough, a mile-long extension of the metre gauge line was put in from Carrol Spring Farm, running southeast between Top Lodge and Westfield Lodge, crossing Mill Lane (now Mill Road) on the level to run down to Rixon's old workings near Broadholme, which were then called No. 6 quarry. Working towards Mill Lane continued in a small way up to 1901, but a more important area on the northwest side of Mill Lane was opened up in 1897; from a trailing junction near Broadholme the tramway was taken under Mill Lane and quarrying started on the north side of the bridge, working away from the latter to east and west. The rather clumsy reversal was obviated a few years later (certainly by 1905) by a through line west of Westfield Lodge, and the level crossing taken out. Much of the ground between Mill Lane and Finedon quarries was leased from the Ecclesiastical Commissioners, the eastern part in Irthlingborough parish through the Dean & Chapter of Peterborough Cathedral.

There were no further major tramway extensions, but branches – some of them quite lengthy – were put in to develop new quarries. In the end, almost the whole of the area bounded by Mill Road, Sidegate Lane, Ryebury Hill and Irthlingborough Road had been worked for ironstone and/or limestone either by quarrying or mining. It was done in piecemeal fashion, though, with the more readily accessible stone being tackled first and the central areas under heavier cover when bigger machines were available. The surveyor's plans of workings from different decades fit together like pieces of a jigsaw puzzle to cover the whole area.

An unusual method of identifying the working faces was used; instead of using a field name or a serial number, a combination of number and location was employed, thus:-

Finedon No. 1
Carrol Spring No. 2
Carrol Spring No. 3

Wellingborough Quarries & Mines.   The first steel skip transporter working with a No. 16 Ruston crane shovel, 1912. Machine is stripping overburden.   Collection Ron Sismey

Wellingborough Quarries & Mines.   Hardly any photographs have survived of the early metre gauge tramway and its equipment, though there are plenty of the system as reconstructed in 1933/4; as a result, we tend to think of it as always being much as it was, say, in the 1950s – which must have been very far from the case. This undated photograph of No. 3 gives us a brief glimpse into those days, when the work was harder and the pay minimal. Note the fireirons on the tank, the headlamp, and the chains for the use of the roperunner.   Collection Greg Evans

Carrol Spring No. 4
Carrol Spring No. 5
Ditchford No. 6
Harrowden No. 8 (commenced 1896)
Ditchford No. 9 (commenced 1898)
Ditchford No. 10 (commenced 1898)
Finedon No. 1A (commenced 1897)
Carrol Spring No. 5A (commenced 1905)

The precise whereabouts of some of the faces have not been determined, and No. 7 seems to have escaped record; those up to No. 6 on the above list were all in existence by 1895. It will be obvious that quarrying activities by the Wellingborough Iron Co Ltd were very widespread within ten years or so of commencement, and subsequent workings were mostly in the gaps. For example, Carrol Spring No. 5 and Ditchford No. 9 faces gradually moved towards each other in the course of time and by the end of World War II the two faces were in line and were collectively known as Wellingborough No. 5 Quarry, though served by separate tramway branches, one on each side of the track to Finedon Top Lodge.

Wellingborough Quarries & Mines. The only one of the earlier batch of locomotives to survive 1933 – for very occasional use as a spare engine – was No. 4, photographed near the locomotive shed on 31st August 1947. Identical in design with No. 3, but less cluttered, and in reasonable condition.

Limestone was obtained from ground north of Carrol Spring farm (some from the Mackworth Dolben lease and some, further north, from a lease made with the Ecclesiastical Commissioners) and from former Stanton leases for which the latter company had been granted the lease for the extraction of ironstone only; Wellingborough Iron Co Ltd purchased this last area from the trustees of the late Miss Mackworth Dolben in 1912. Finally, for the nineteenth century period, a small area north of the furnaces was leased for 14 years from Earl Fitzwilliam; this was opened up but in fact no great quantity of ironstone was obtained, as it was an isolated patch surviving between the valleys eroded by the Ise and the brook running past the ironworks.

With the passage of time it became necessary to tackle greater depths of overburden to the north and east of the area already developed; in some cases, as at Carrol Spring No. 5 quarry, between Top Lodge farm and the Irthlingborough road – also known as Cooper's pit – a navvy and conveyor were introduced to deal with some 24 feet of overburden, the stone being loaded by hand. These machines were supplied in 1912, the navvy designated in Ruston Proctor's records as 16 ton, but in Stanton's files as a No. 18 navvy; this worked in conjunction a skip conveyor designed by Ruston Proctor and Fraser & Chalmers, with a truck capable of holding 2½ cubic yards of spoil, running on a lattice 'bridge' 116 feet long, 45 feet above the line. The situation further east was however complicated by two geological faults that left the company no option but to mine – this being before the days of massive draglines of course. It will be recalled that Neilson, on the adjoining property to the west, had resorted to mining in 1909, but with indifferent success. Wellingborough Iron Co Ltd tackled the problem more efficiently by putting in charge Carl Steiner, a German who had previously had mining experience at Islip, and he arrived in 1911. There is no doubt of his efficiency, for his mining methods worked very successfully – but he was inclined to brag of German superiority in these matters, which made him unpopular – to the extent that he was nearly 'strung up' at the Mason's Arms in 1914! He was interned as an enemy alien and never returned to Thingdon.

The output of Thingdon mine (Wellingborough assumed the former Neilson name, which is an early form of Finedon) continued to pass down Neilson's tramway, and when Wellingborough Iron Co started mining elsewhere they continued to use underground tramways of 2ft 4ins gauge. This was early in 1922, by which time the Glebe quarry (an extension of Finedon No. 1, commenced in 1914) was having to deal with forty feet of overburden by means of a steam navvy and a transporter; headings were driven eastwards from the quarry face towards the Neilson area and in 1923 the headings joined those of Thingdon. In 1920 the company purchased Finedon Glebe (presumably it had only been leased before) which included the Glebe mines and quarries and Carrol Spring farm. Mr A.H. Wells, who started work in the quarries in 1908, stated that there were about 150 men working underground in teams of two, the usual procedure; and fourteen horses, stabled in Ivy Lane in Finedon village. The type of wagon used in the mines in the early days is not known – other than that the bodies were made of wood – but a body of what is presumed to be one of these still survived in 1967 in the derelict mining area between Glebe quarry and No. 6 quarry; it was very small, of triangular cross section, 24 ins wide x 17 ins long x 10 ins deep, and fitted with trunnions of side-tipping. There were no handles, but with a wagon as small as this they were probably not required. This wagon would presumably derive from the 1900–1928 period, and may well have been one of Neilson's (see under the Thingdon Mines section); the relic was swept away in the big 'mine entrance' cleanup of 1976/7.

There was also a small mine reached by an adit in a face near Carrol Spring farm, on the north side of Sidegate Lane; this was opened about 1924, and the tramway was presumably also of 2ft 4ins gauge, worked by horses. There were several headings and the output was taken to a tipping arrangement on to the metre gauge line. This mine did not last long, and it and the adjacent quarry area was filled in about 1927 to field level by the local council, and was then planted with ash and pine trees.

With the two main mines connected up and collectively referred to as Thingdon, opportunity was taken to introduce an improved haulage system, which took place in 1928. New main-and-tail haulage was installed in the mine, driven by a steam winding engine near the entrance to one of the Glebe headings, and terminating at a brick-built tipping dock at the end of the metre gauge tramway coming in from the direction of Carrol Spring farm. There was a frightful gradient up from the entrance to No. 1 quarry, and the locomotives must have had to work very hard – as also they must have done in purely quarrying days. However, these arrangements only lasted four years, the ironworks, quarries and mines all being closed in September 1932 as a result of the Depression.

Quarrying was continued during the period of mining, but on a much reduced scale; the Ditchford quarries (Nos 9 and 10) were worked until 1921, and the Carrol Spring quarries Nos 2 and 3 to 1932. They were partly on leasehold and partly on freehold land. In Ditchford No 10 quarry the cover was removed by navvy, the ironstone by hand.

Limestone was also quarried north of Carrol Spring farm, and also (about 1920) from Neilson's old limestone quarry northeast of the 'green lane', but by 1930 nearly all the limestone under light cover had been extracted; it is Oolite limestone, not Lincolnshire, and hereabouts somewhat variable in composition. The Premier Cement Co Ltd, whose Irthlingborough quarries lay east of Ditchford No 9 quarry, commenced operations about the same time as the latter, but the works closed in 1928, perhaps because they had difficulty in processing. Wellingborough Iron Co Ltd leased a small quarry near Stanwick in 1930, the output being conveyed by lorry to a tipping dock at Irthlingborough station; in earlier years Butlins had obtained supplies from here (see under the Chelveston section).

During the trade depression of the late twenties a single furnace only was in blast and on 22nd September 1932 work ceased altogether, the mines and quarries being closed; at the same time Stanton Ironworks Co Ltd and Wellingborough Iron Co Ltd came to a working agreement replacing the earlier arrangements that by then had become rather complicated, and the Stanton company assumed a greater measure of control that crystallized in a complete rebuilding of the ironworks on modern lines, a reorganization of the quarries and mines, and a remodelling of the brickworks that adjoined the ironworks to the south, obtaining its supplies from the Upper Lias clay in the immediate vicinity. Brook farm had been purchased in 1920, giving the company more land south of the works, including that over which passed the narrow gauge tramway.

A thorough survey of the ironstone area was carried out so that the future supplies to the two new blast furnaces would be assured; this included a renewal of the lease with the Ecclesiastical Commissioners for 60 years from 29th September 1933. Up till then the system of geological faults (Carrol Spring and White Lodge faults) was only imperfectly known, and the new knowledge led to the driving of a new adit and the installation of a completely new haulage system. The 2ft 4ins gauge track was retained in the mines and the existing (from 1928) squarish steel tubs, but these were pulled by Ruston & Hornsby diesel locomotives; it was planned that, should the increasing length of track underground prove uneconomical for the locomotives, electrically worked endless haulage would be used instead – but this was not done, the Rustons working to the end of mining operations. Double track from the heading ran up an incline to a gantry, and here the trucks were run by gravity over a weighbridge and then emptied by an electrically-operated tippler into wagons standing on a siding near the terminus of a new metre gauge branch from Carrol Spring farm – surrounded by growing corn! The branch was practically level, thus obviating the difficulties attendent on the steep gradient of the old route; the new adit was also at a higher level than the old Finedon Glebe quarry, and lay south of the 1928 adit, which was retained for the use of men entering the mine. The headings were 14–15 feet wide and 8–8½ feet high, with very little timbering being required; the internal headings were one chain apart, with the main haulage way running east-south-east.

New large four-wheeled wagons carrying pairs of skips on steel underframes were supplied by G.R. Turner Ltd of Langley Mill, each skip carrying a nominal five tons of ore (though in practice 12–15 tons were

Wellingborough Quarries & Mines. The new adit to Wellingborough mines photographed in the course of an official tour of inspection by company directors, 1933. Note the light 2ft 4ins gauge track.   BSC

often loaded into a pair); these wagons had centre buckeye couplings, as had the two powerful new 0-6-OST locomotives with 10 ins cylinders supplied by Peckett & Sons Ltd to replace the old four-wheelers, one of which was retained as a spare. There were also hopper wagons with

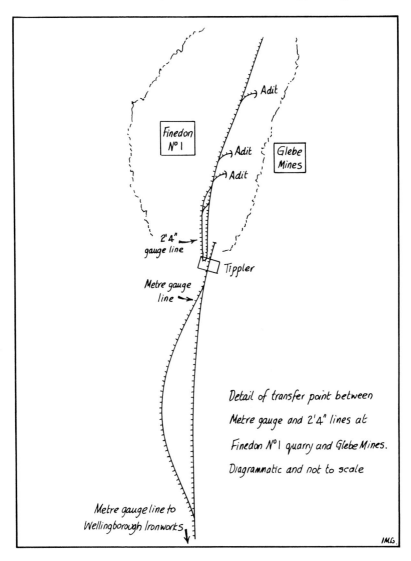

Finedon
Nº 1

Adit

Adit

Glebe
Mines

Adit

2'4"
gauge line

Tippler

Metre gauge
line

Detail of transfer point between
Metre gauge and 2'4" lines at
Finedon Nº 1 quarry and Glebe Mines.
Diagrammatic and not to scale

Metre gauge line to
Wellingborough Ironworks

IMG.

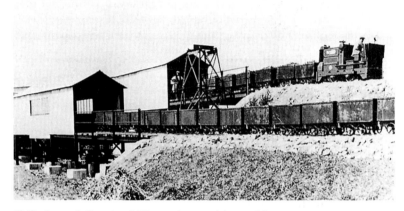

Wellingborough Quarries & Mines. An essential part of the new narrow gauge tramway system was the transfer of ore from the 2ft 4ins mines tubs via rotary tipplers into metre gauge skips for transit to the furnaces. These two views show the installation concerned, with (above) a Ruston locomotive pushing loaded wagons into the upper tippler, with empties waiting to be collected from the lower level; and (below) a train of metre gauge wagons awaiting loading. 1934. Stanton Ironworks Co. Ltd.

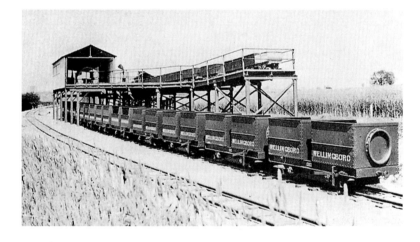

Wellingborough Quarries & Mines. One of the standard wagons carrying a pair of skips, each of which held a nominal five tons of ore. 13th June 1962.   S.A. Leleux

Wellingborough Quarries & Mines. The new metre gauge line was operated by three Peckett locomotives, two of 1934 and a larger one of 1942. The picture shows P 1870 of the first pair, which carried no names or numbers. This was taken on 16th April 1938, with the engine in her original Peckett livery, and is interesting in showing her with a train of hopper wagons instead of the usual skip wagons (as on the line at the rear).

G. Alliez/Courtesy B.D. Stoyel

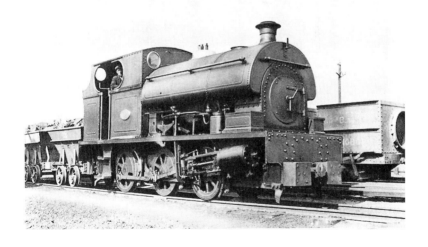

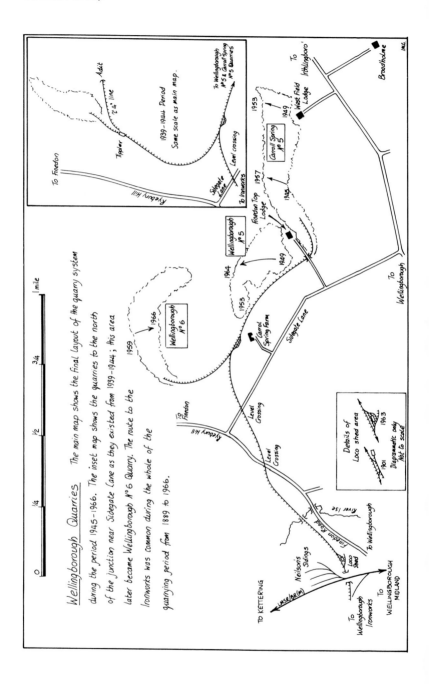

Wellingborough Quarries The main map shows the final layout of the quarry system during the period 1945–1966. The inset map shows the quarries to the north of the junction near Sidegate Lane as they existed from 1939–1944; this area later became Wellingborough N° 6 Quarry. The route to the Ironworks was common during the whole of the quarrying period from 1889 to 1966.

sloping slides, possibly used for limestone. The main tramway was relaid throughout with heavier track to cope with the increased weight of the trains. This represented the last sustained attempt in the ironstone industry to modernise a narrow gauge system, and since that date – and indeed some time before – it had been the custom to allow them to carry on in their existing condition or to replace them by standard gauge. At the ironworks the skips, which were fitted with trunnions, were lifted by means of a 'Goliath' crane and the ore was tipped on to a clamp for calcining; the crane, which travelled over the clamps, was also fitted with a grab for handling the calcined ore.

While the emphasis in this period was on mining, opencast quarrying continued at Carrol Spring farm and at Ditchford, but with the benefit of mechanical equipment both for baring (removing overburden) and loading of ironstone. The ore first quarried at Carrol Spring was outcrop stone of a warm brown colour, but under increasing cover changed to a green form, like the mined ore. Quarrying of limestone ceased in the early 1930s as the beds lay under a depth of overburden it was considered uneconomic to remove.

Wellingborough Quarries & Mines. The 1942 locomotive was bigger than the 1934 pair, with a shorter chimney the most obvious feature. Coaling was always hard work, whatever the size of the loco Shed in the background. 26th November 1964. S.A. Leleux

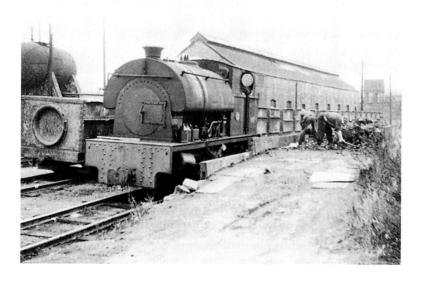

In 1942 a third and even more powerful Peckett locomotive with 12in. cylinders (but, again, no buffers) was purchased, together with more wagons from G.R. Turner Ltd, bringing the total of these to 98; this of course was to provide the extra output required by wartime conditions. Also during the war, larger quarrying equipment was obtained to deal with the development of Wellingborough No. 5 quarry, derived from Carrol Spring No. 5 and Ditchford No. 9 quarries; these were respectively northwest and southeast of Top Lodge farm, and when both faces were north of the latter, they were in line, though still separated by the farm road past Top Lodge. The new machines included the pioneer 5W walking dragline with Ward Leonard electric control, for stripping overburden; and a 55RB high-lift crawler shovel for loading. The former was erected in 1939–40 and the latter arrived in February 1941. These eventually led to the abandonment of mining, which is believed to have taken place in 1944, and thenceforward all working was opencast.

After the war demand slackened to some extent but the usual practice was to have two locomotives in steam, with the third spare or under repair, and this system continued right to the end. Within this framework however there was a good deal of variation in day-to-day practice, and on some days only one locomotive would be used – depending on demand or availability. When No. 5 quarry alone was being worked (after the cessation of mining, that is) one locomotive would work between quarry and locomotive shed, where the second locomotive would take over the train and take it on to the calcine bank at the ironworks; this locomotive had only a short main line trip but was doubtless kept busy moving the wagons at the calcine bank. On 1st January 1959 No. 6 quarry further north, an opencast extension of Glebe mines, was brought into use, while production continued at No. 5; as a result, the two locomotives took up similar duties, each dealing with one quarry and working right through to the ironworks. By 1962 only Wellingborough No. 6 quarry (to give it its full title) was operating, and a further variation in practice ensued with one locomotive working from pit to Carrol Spring Farm sidings, and the other taking over there for the longer run to the ironworks. By this time Wellingborough ironworks were no longer using ore from their own quarries, which was found not to be the most suitable, and were 'importing' ore from Corby; though in any event closure of the ironworks was close at hand. The Wellingborough quarry output of two thousand tons per week was being sent to Lancashire Steel Corporation, Irlam, and for them the ore was sent away raw, and therefore working of the calcine

Wellingborough Quarries & Mines. The first Ruston-Bucyrus/Monighan 5W walking dragline put to work in Britain, 2nd March 1940. The bridge shown carries the farm track to Finedon Top Lodge.   B S C

Wellingborough Quarries & Mines. Carrol Spring No. 5 quarry, 31st July 1956, with the 5W walking dragline stripping overburden and 55RB shovel at the ironstone face. Beyond the 5W can be seen the face of Ditchford No. 9 quarry; later, these two faces were united to form one long face known as Wellingborough No. 5 quarry.   B S C

bank no longer required, once the stocks had been cleared.

There was also the complication of coaling and watering; there was a water supply at No. 6 pit but no coal, and the locomotive at the quarry had to return to the shed for supplies at lunch time, afterwards working back up to the pit along with the 'main line' engine, taking a set of empties. On occasion, too, the engine had to get water from the shed, with a mid-morning trip to do this. There was no strict demarcation in duties between the three locomotives: P 2029 was more powerful and heavier than the others and the tendency was to use her on the main line where the track was better laid and to use her advantages on the bank, up and down. She did, however, work in the pits when required.

There had been a change in the handling methods at the calcine bank, too, where the crane came to grief when the driver did not apply the brake quickly enough, and the lifting mechanism went over the end of the steel supporting structure to form a tangled steel wreck from which the driver escaped with a sprained ankle! A mobile crane was brought in to do the work. This accident is believed to have occurred about 1952.

The status of the ironworks declined as the 1960's approached, and for two years at the end of the 1950's only one furnace was in blast; in February 1960 the second furnace was relit, but only for a year, and it was clear that the end was in sight. The falling demand for pig iron was

Wellingborough Quarries & Mines.
The water tower at the loco. shed, with ladder and 'office' beneath.
G.H. Starmer

Wellingborough Quarries & Mines. No. 6 quarry, 18th August 1966. Locomotive No. 86 stands with a train of skips being loaded by the 55RB high-lift shovel. 5W walking dragline stripping overburden. The pipeline carries compressed air for the drills.

G.H. Starmer

responsible, and as this could be met easily from other ironworks under Stewarts & Lloyds control, closure of Wellingborough was inevitable; the remaining furnace was blown out 23rd October 1962 and the works were officially closed on Wednesday 29th October 1962, on which date all aspects of the ore transfer system came under the control of Stewarts & Lloyds Minerals Ltd. The narrow gauge locomotives had been owned by this company (or a subsidiary) for some years previously, but maintenance, men and general facilities were provided by the ironworks, and in effect the narrow gauge system continued as before, its activities integrated with that of the works it was built to serve. From 29th October 1962 however, matters were different; there was the five-year contract to supply ore to Irlam, so continuation of quarrying was assured. It is interesting to read the comments of visitors to the site in the early 1960's; to all of them it was pretty obvious that quarrying here had only a limited future, but estimates of life varied widely, and the possibility of quarrying west of the Finedon road was mentioned, to be worked either by a standard gauge line or by 'Euclid' dumpers. Neither of these were put into effect of course and for the remainder of its working life the metre gauge system, which had been well laid and carefully maintained, functioned perfectly well. One feature of Wellingborough believed to be unique as far as narrow gauge ironstone lines is concerned, is the use of concrete sleepers that were introduced during World War II at the

Wellingborough Quarries & Mines. View towards Carrol Spring Farm sidings, from the line to the tip. The Wellingborough tramway is believed to be unique among ironstone lines in having some concrete sleepers, as shown here. Note also the catch point. 1st September 1965.
S.A. Leleux

ironworks end, and elsewhere as required for replacements.

Demolition of the ironworks commenced very soon after the closure, and was completed in mid-1964, the site being sold to Wellingborough Urban District Council as from 28th September 1964 for redevelopment as a trading estate, but leaving an area for the transfer of ore to standard gauge railway wagons. One of the first tasks was to connect the electricity supply for the quarry machines to the national grid, now that the power generated at the ironworks was no longer available. This done, quarrying recommenced and trains continued to roll down the track through the narrow-bore tunnel under the BR line, with its admonition to employees to "wait until the smoke has cleared". The ore for Irlam was not calcined, as already mentioned, nor was it crushed, hence the ore-crusher was not used after the closure of Wellingborough furnace, and was dismantled in 1964. Ore transfer suffered a further change, too; a crawler dragline was used, creeping along the centre line of the vacated calcine bank, lifting the skips and tipping them at a very low angle of the jib into standard gauge wagons. This system was further modified in the summer of 1965

Wellingborough Quarries & Mines.   The tunnel under the BR line. Note the check rail on the sharp curve, and the notice exhorting drivers to 'wait until the smoke has cleared'. 2nd July 1957.   J.A. Peden

Wellingborough Quarries & Mines. A train at the unloading point at the ironworks sidings, on 17th August 1966, with the skips being lifted by a 54RB crane for emptying into BR tipplers, at right, for transit to Corby. Wellingborough ironworks had been closed.   G.H. Starmer

when the standard gauge line to the calcine bank, left in by Stewarts & Lloyds to accommodate ore wagons, was lifted and replaced by a transfer point on the site of the old crusher, the narrow gauge layout remaining unaltered. Weighing had been carried out on the weighbridge attached to the ironworks, but this too eventually disappeared in the demolition. As all the old ironworks locomotive stock had been cut up or were not workable, a locomotive had been imported from Glendon in the shape of CARMARTHEN, to shunt the standard gauge wagons; under the revised arrangement, a weighbridge was put in at another point, such that the BR locomotive could push in the wagons to the top of the siding; when full, they were allowed to run by gravity over the weighbridge down to the yard for collection by BR. CARMARTHEN then returned to Glendon in October 1964.

Locomotive operation did not alter much, with two in service – usually P 2029 on the main line and one of the others in the quarry. Indeed, from the quarrying side, there was nothing different at all. Coaling was by hand from a standard gauge wagon at the ironworks, the quarry locomotive going down for this purpose about midday. Another light engine trip to the shed was for breakfast for, like all ironstone quarries, the day started very early, at 6.00am; at 8.45 both locos would be at the shed, while the crews fried eggs and bacon in a small building under the water tower.

The long-lived Wellingborough No. 5 quarry, which was in operation as Carrol Spring No. 5 quarry well before 1900, finally closed the week before August Bank Holiday 1964, the track was lifted and the ground bulldozed over; only to become a licensed 'tip' for Rushden council, whose lorries used the trackbed from the bridge leading to Top Lodge. Curiously, the quarry noticeboard, lettered WELLINGBOROUGH No. 5 QUARRY was transferred to the last working pit, No. 6, with the number unaltered!

We have mentioned the locomotives more or less in passing when referring to their duties, and indeed our information is practically confined to those that came with the 1933 scheme of reorganization. Only one of the earlier stock, WELLINGBOROUGH No. 4, survived as a spare and she was very little used, at any rate after the war; she could handle only six Turner wagons against the Peckett's eight. Nevertheless she was fitted with a commodious home-made cab of welded steel sheets about 1951, to replace the sparse original; but a year or so later she was dumped outside the shed by the steaming ponds, and worked no more. On 25th September 1959 she was moved to a place by the ore crusher and

Wellingborough Quarries & Mines.   No. 86 pushing empty skips to No. 6 quarry on 17th August 1966. There was no reversing loop here.   G.H. Starmer

Wellingborough Quarries & Mines.   P 2029 at Carrol Spring Farm sidings, pushing the wagons over the weighbridge. 28th August 1963.   P.H. Groom

Wellingborough Quarries & Mines. A roadside scene once very typical of the ironstone quarries. No. 86 with a loaded train from Carrol Spring Farm sidings approaches Sidegate Lane crossing, 17th August 1966.   G.H. Starmer

Wellingborough Quarries & Mines. Once a familiar sight to travellers on the road from Wellingborough to Finedon, P 2029 hauls a train over the level crossing on its way to the furnaces, 28th August 1963. The flagman stands in front of the first wagon.   P.H. Groom

scrapped piecemeal over the next six months. Her livery was green, lined black edged yellow, and she had one embellishment denied the Pecketts – a cast brass nameplate with red-backed lettering. The anonymity of the three Pecketts has always seemed to us a curious and regrettable omission; contrary to practice at the ironworks and to Stanton's policy of naming their narrow gauge locomotives. The Pecketts were handsome machines and photogenic unadorned; but how much nicer had they been given local names on brass plates. It was not until Stewarts & Lloyds Minerals Ltd took over that matters improved. Originally they carried Peckett's standard livery of Brunswick green lined black edged yellow, with red rods, and 2029 (at least) had not had a repaint by 1960 – nor, possibly, the others. In 1961 however, 1870 was repainted plain light green; and early in 1963 all three were sporting buffer beams repainted red edged with yellow (inside) and black (outside), as well as having plastic tablets bearing the 'plant numbers' allotted by Stewarts & Lloyds Minerals – 8315/85–87 in works number order. The next addition was in mid-1964, when 6 ins. white figures on the cabside were applied, and finally in the week ending 12th February 1965 (when the pits happened to be idle) all three were painted in full Stewarts & Lloyds Minerals livery of dark green with black top to the bunker and handrail backing, and 'S & L MINERALS LTD No. 8X in white on the bunker. They were then the smartest they had ever been as a trio and were well kept then to the end. All had spark arrestors (as the trains traversed cornfields), that of 87 being the 'chip basket' type, and others having straight-sided mesh. 87 had a shrill whistle, 85/6 chimes. 87 had a final repaint in May 1966, as her regular driver was retiring. It is pleasing to note that all three are now preserved, at the Northamptonshire Ironstone Railway Trust at Hunsbury Hill and by the Irchester Narrow Gauge Railway Trust in Irchester country park.

Brief reference has been made to the early mining tubs, from remains discovered on the site in 1967; there was also a pair of small wagons, one V-shaped and one U-shaped, derelict by the 'Dairy' (on the track from Finedon Road) in 1966. Those in use from 1928 onwards were squarish steel tubs, as illustrated, in conjunction with Ruston & Hornsby diesel locomotives. The mines locomotives were all by this maker, the first one coming secondhand from Stanton's ironstone mine at Holwell, near Melton Mowbray; she was 16HP class with a Lister 18/2 engine, and proved very successful. As a result, other machines followed but were of 30 horsepower. Although RH 172888 was of class 22/28HP and RH

174140 and 177608 were class 27/32 HP, all had Lister 3JP engines, the difference in classification being merely a 'paper' one introduced by the makers. The final locomotive was styled 25/30HP class, with a Ruston 3VSO engine. The livery of these locomotives was dark olive green with a black line edged with white, with the Ruston coat of arms on the body, and the earlier ones with 'RUSTON' transferred along the sides. As mines locomotives, they were fitted with exhaust filters and had no cabs.

The 'main line' wagons have also been mentioned; the total was said to be 98, each consisting of a steel frame carrying a pair of skips, painted black with the number stencilled in white; the capacity of each skip was nominally five tons, i.e. ten tons for the full wagon, but in practice the tonnage averaged around 13. In the course of time a few wagons were converted to other uses; 17,49, and 94 were flat wagons for carrying quarrying equipment, and 96 was flat, but with a low wooden frame for holding coal. There was also an ash wagon kept at the locomotive shed, with a shallow steel container with two doors opening on one side, mounted on a tub underframe. These wagons were all built by G.R. Turner Ltd, the earlier ones with a rectangular makers plate, and the later ones an oval plate with the 1942 date of manufacture included; these last did not form a consecutive batch in the numerical series, but included numbers between 2 and 88 – suggesting perhaps that they were not numbered until after 1942. At the end, four (1, 17, 38, 55) were repainted red, and by this time some cannibalization had occurred, with non-matching pairs of skips. Under S & L M ownership the wagons were given plant numbers 8559/50/XX, the last two digits corresponding to the numbers stencilled on the skips. Wagon repairs appear to have been carried out in the locomotive shed latterly, but whether this was always the practice is not known.

There was also at least one wooden wagon underframe and wheels, rather like those at Scaldwell, and used in 1965 for carrying large diameter hoses in connection with pumping activities at the quarry. During the last year of operation considerable trouble was encountered from water seepage from the old mines that had been broached in extending No. 6 quarry; this was minimized by damming – but the end was in sight anyway. On completion of the Lancashire Steel Corporation contract the output had gone to Corby, which was rather a 'coals to Newcastle' arrangement, and on 1st March 1966 it was decided to cease operations in October; though rumours of closure had been in the local press for the previous two years. The 'running down' process then

Wellingborough Quarries & Mines. No. 87 takes a loaded train over the river Ise, towards the ironworks, 21st September 1965. M.J. Leah

commenced, and by August two locomotives were in steam only on Mondays and Tuesdays, and one loco. in steam on Wednesdays, the other driver operating the crane transferring ore to standard gauge wagons. Some cutting-up of redundant wagons took place.

For the last few weeks the locomotives in traffic were 85 and 87, 85 working between the quarry (the gradient out of which now about one in twenty) and Carrol Spring Farm sidings, and 87 between the latter and BR. In the final week, one observer noted 87 bringing eight full wagons down from the quarries, stopping just above the river bridge for the brakes to be taken off, and then run briskly past the shed under the BR lines. The same two locomotives were employed on a farewell tour organised by the Birmingham Locomotive Club, with the Industrial Railway Society and Narrow Gauge Railway Society on 1st October, when some two hundred members and friends participated in a ride over the line, with 85 leading and 87 pushing. Such occasions are enjoyable yet tinged with sadness for their unrepeatability; and at the conclusion of the tour the dark clouds that had been gathering during the morning released heavy rain to accompany the final rites of the locomotives returning to the shed.

Wellingborough Quarries & Mines.   On 1st October 1966 a party of Industrial Railway Society members was granted the pleasure of a farewell tour of the quarry railway, using locomotives Nos. 85 and 87. The photograph shows the train just above the bridge over the Ise. Jean Pugh

The last day of production was 14th October, and a photograph of 87 bringing down the last load was taken for the Corby archives by Mr Harris. Dismantlement and restoration commenced immediately, part of the track near the quarry office was lifted to allow access for vehicles filling No. 6 quarry, and the diggers (a Ruston Bucyrus 5W and a 55RB) were dumped beside the line near Sidegate Lane for breaking up. This fate, happily, did not extend to the locomotives, which had survived long enough to interest the preservation movement, and on 1st December all three of them were in steam at the shed and arranged in expected order of disposal; it was said that they were sold for £600 each. Some track was sold also. Even some of the tubs from the surviving wagons were saved, being transferred to Cranford for use in connection with calcining; it was suggested in fact that their symmetrical section gave them an advantage over the normal open-ended type, in that they could be discharged either way. The rest of the wagon stock was assembled at Carrol Spring Farm sidings, where it was cut up early in 1967, commencing in February. By this time nearly all the track had been lifted apart from that at the level crossings and some at the locomotive shed where 86 and 87 were awaiting collection. The level crossings were tarmaced over in the early Spring, and lineside fences removed below Sidegate Lane. At the BR end

Wellingborough Quarries & Mines.   Tramway route to Finedon No. 1 quarry (left) and to 1933 adit (right). 19th April 1978.   Eric Tonks

the whole area was incorporated in the trading estate that had earlier covered the ironworks site. The water tower at the loco. shed was demolished in July 1967 but the building itself was painted white and became the office of Tingdene Homes; from here the embankment towards the Finedon Road was still (1970) in position, including the bridge over the Ise, as were the crossing-keeper's cabin and the tunnel under BR. Otherwise, most of the route had been restored. The Ise bridge was dismantled at the end of July 1975 and later that year a 40-foot section of the embankment just above the Ise was cleared when a sewage pipe was laid.

The physical remains present a curious mixture of chance survivals and almost complete obliteration, but until 1976 were far more extensive than they are today. Of Rixon's original tramway along Ryebury Hill it is fair to say that no recognisable traces are to be seen; the road still has a grass verge wide enough to accommodate a narrow gauge tramway, but that is all. The 1933 Wellingborough line at first left some momentoes, however, particularly from the BR tunnel up to the Finedon road, including the locomotive shed and most of the embankment east of the road. The shed was acquired by Tingdene Homes, a firm of caravan dealers, but was pulled down in September 1982, the tunnel under BR was very effectively sealed by pressure-filling with concrete and covering the ends with soil, and the general site made into a trading estate. At the level crossing the keeper's hut is now a ruin, but there is a gate on the north side of the road. Beyond Finedon Road the course of the line has been returned to agricultural use, at ground level as it was, but can be picked up again in the vicinity of Carrol Spring Farm. Beyond that the tramway remains date back well before the 1933 revival.

It is clear that there was no provision in the original Wellingborough leases for restoration of the land, which was left as the operators finished with it, a jumble of heaps and gullies – some pretty deep – and fields threaded by trackbeds and pockmarked by mine subsidences. As we shall see, many of these traces have now gone, but sufficient remains to enable us to snatch a glimpse into things past. The best place to start is by approaching along the farm track to the 'Dairy' (shown as 'pumping station' on the OS maps), at the far end of which the path drops down to the southern end of the former No. 1 quarry, which stretches in a north-north-easterly direction for nearly a third of a mile, the gullet sloping downwards as the land surface rises. The banks are considerably overgrown and the western (restored) side was planted in 1933 with conifers, but the familiar pattern of a terminal gullet is plain enough; but it does not take much imagination to appreciate the difficulties of working a quarry of this depth (80–100 feet) with the limited mechanical aids available before World War I. There was a very heavy overburden to be shifted, and then a stiff bank up which the loaded trains had to climb to reach Carrol Spring farm sidings to the south. When mining commenced, the output went out via Neilson's tramway for some years, as we have seen, but by 1933 used this route out of No. 1 quarry. There seem to have been four headings into the mines; these have now all been filled in but the site of the main adit could be gauged from the presence in the gullet of a concrete block (with some projecting ironwork) where the steam winding engine was placed. The filling later fell away and in 1983 one could peer into the brick-lined adit. A little to the south some crumbling brickwork marked the site of the tipping dock. Along the eastern margin of the southern part of No. 1 quarry can be seen the trackbed leading to the adit for the 1933 mining operations, but there is nothing to be seen of the adit itself. There are other traces between here and No. 6 quarry, but too fragmentary for full interpretation. There were many 'cave-ins' and depressions in the ground between No. 1 quarry gullet, No. 6 quarry and Neville's Lodge, mostly surrounded by rough wooden fences (some very rough indeed, so that the sites can still be identified); but these were all filled in in 1976/7 at the same time as the very clear-cut remains of Thingdon quarries and mines (Neilson, later Wellingborough Iron Co Ltd) were bulldozed out of existence. It would seem likely that traces of Wellingborough quarrying activities will remain for a long time to come however, and depressions are general over the whole mining area. No. 5 quarry was in 1977 being filled in with rubbish by Rushden council, but this operation ceased after the western end had been filled – the eastern portion, beyond Top Lodge, remained intact in 1985. On the other hand, No. 6 quarry was designated 'Sidegate Lane Landfill Site' by Northamptonshire county council; the lorries used part of the tramway trackbed and filling had progressed well by 1985, with the surface contours rounded.

The site of Carrol Spring farm sidings is still clear and the course of the line to Top Lodge is very well defined between hedges. The driveway to Top Lodge crossed the tramway by a girder bridge, still in position in 1977, the girders supported on brick pillars and surmounted by a wooden fence; unfortunately, in 1978 the bridge was filled in beneath. East of the bridge the route has been levelled and larch plantations on hill-and-dale

Wellingborough Quarries & Mines. Surface view between No. 1 and No. 6 quarries, 19th April 1978. The fence at right surrounds a 'sink hole'; the depression in the centre of the picture might be a former tramway route, or a line of subsidence.
Eric Tonks

Thingdon Mines. 'Sink hole' showing subsidence over old mining tunnel, 24th March 1977. Spoil bank of Wellingborough No. 6 quarry at rear. Eric Tonks

Wellingborough Quarries & Mines. Parapet of bridge by Westfield Lodge, on the south side of the road to Irthlingborough. 19th April 1978. Eric Tonks

119

are to be seen; and sunken fields up to Mill Road (Wellingborough–Irthlingborough). There is a bridge under this road, the parapets being of brick with concrete capping; these parapets were rebuilt in 1965. On the west side the tramway route has been filled in, also the branch that tunneled beneath the drive to Westfield Lodge. Beyond here, on the east, i.e. towards Ditchford, was a wooden shed with a long slatted louvre, which was a stable in Rixon's day. This building was leased to a farmer and was in excellent condition, and the course of the trackbed to it was still plain, though the outcrop quarrying area had long been smoothed over. Regrettably, this fine relic was also swept away, probably in 1982. With that, we wend our way back to Wellingborough.

Footnotes

1.   Thanks to Mr A.St G. Walsh for this information.

Grid References

Rixon's Tramway

903692	Tipping Dock
908695	Bridge over Ise
905692	Finedon Road crossing
916707	Tramway terminus

Wellingborough Iron Co Tramway

903694	Tipping dock at Ironworks
904695	Tunnel under LMSR (east end)
905695	Locomotive Shed
907697	Bridge over Ise
910699	Level crossing – Finedon Road
914701	Level crossing – Sidegate Lane
917701	Carrol Spring Farm Sidings
918711	Adit for Glebe Mines, pre 1933
918708	Tipping dock to metre line, pre 1933
919709	New adit
919708	Exchange point between 2ft 4ins tramway and metre tramway (after 1933)
919713	No 1 quarry, north end
919708	Site of cavities
922697	Bridge to Top Lodge
932695	Tunnel by Westfield Lodge
932693	Stables by Broadholme

Locomotives

Gauge: 1 Metre (but see text)

No. 1	0-4-OST	OC HE	348	1884	9 x 14ins	2ft 4½ ins	New 7/1884	(1)
No. 2	0-4-OST	OC HE	405	1887	9 x 14ins	2ft 4½ ins	New 1/1887	(2)
No. 4	O-4-OST	OC HE	473	1888	10 x 16ins	2ft 6½ ins	New 12/1888	Scr 10/1959
No. 1	0-4-OST	OC HE	562	1892	10 x 16ins	2ft 6½ ins	New 4/1892	Scr C. 1933
No. 3	0-4-OST	OC HE	603	1894	10 x 16ins	2ft 6½ ins	New 2/1894	Scr C. 1933
No. 10	0-4-OST	OC WB	1942	1918	8 x 12ins	2ft 0½ ins	New 5/1918	Scr C. 1934
No. 85 (from 1964)	0-6-OST	OC P	1870	1934	10 x 18ins	3ft 0ins	New 9/1934	(3)
No. 86 (from 1964)	0-6-OST	OC P	1871	1934	10 x 18ins	3ft 0ins	New 9/1934	(4)
No. 87 (from 1964)	0-6-OST	OC P	2029	1942	12 x 20ins	3ft 0½ ins	New 11/1942	(5)

(1) to T. Oliver, Totley, 1892; then to Penmon Park Quarries, Anglesey, 1904
(2) to T. Oliver, contractor, Rishworth, 1898
(3) to Alan Bloom, Bressingham Hall, Norfolk, 12/1966
(4) to John R. Billows, Pytchley Road Industrial Estate, Kettering, 6/1967. To Northamptonshire Ironstone Railway Trust, Hunsbury Hill, 6/1975
(5) to F.G. Cann & Son, Thrapston Road, Finedon, 8/1967; to N.I.R.T. 6/1975

Gauge: 2ft 4ins

No. 1	4wDM	RH	168831	1933	16HP class. 2¾ ton	(a)	(1)
No. 2	4wDM	RH	172888	1934	22/28HP class .4 ton	New 8/1934	(2)
No. 3	4wDM	RH	174140	1935	27/32HP class. 4 ton	New 2/1935	(3)
No. 4	4wDM	RH	177608	1936	27/32HP class. 4 ton	New 8/1936	(4)
No. 5	4wDM	RH	200494	1940	25/30HP class. 4 ton	New 12/1940	(5)

(a) ex Stanton Ironworks Co Ltd, Holwell Mines, 1934

(1) to Wreake Sand & Gravel Co Ltd, Asfordby, Leicestershire
(2) to Nuthall sandpits, Nottinghamshire
(3) to South Witham Quarries 6/1947
(4) converted to compressor unit and later sent to South Witham Quarries
(5) to Bowne & Shaw Ltd, Wirksworth, Derbyshire 6/1947

Gauge: 4ft 8½ins

50 CARMARTHEN	0-6-OST	IC K	5478	1936	16 x 22 ins 3ft 6ins	(a)	(1)

(a) ex Glendon East Quarries c 1/1964

(1)   to Glendon East Quarries 10/1964

Quarry Machines

No. 18 S. Shovel	RP	340	1912	¼ Cu.Yd.		New 3/1912	(1)
Skip Transporter			1912			(a)	(2)
Skip Transporter			1912			(b)	(3)
S. Navvy	Wh		1915(?)			(c)	(4)
No. 20 S. Stripping Shovel	RP	435	1915	1¼ Cu. Yds.	55ft	New 7/1915	(5)
No. 20 S. Shovel	RH	528	1918	2¼ Cu.Yds.	31ft	(d)	(6)
5W DE. Walking Dragline	RB	4372	1939	3 Cu.Yds.	135ft	New 11/1939	(7)
No. 4 55RB E. Shovel. High lift. Crawler.	RB	5665	1941	2½ Cu.Yds.	29ft	New 2/1941	(8)
21RB D. Dragline	RB	2511	1934	¾ Cu.Yd.	40ft	(e)	(9)
No. 23 No. 4 D. Shovel	RH or RB					(f)	(10)
No. 20 S. Shovel	RH	505	1918	2¼ Cu.Yds.	31ft	(g)	s/s
D. Dragline. Crawler. Lima						(h)	(11)
54RB D. Dragline	RB	8017	1944			(i)	(12)

(a)   Made by Heenan & Froude Ltd, Worcester, to RP specification.
(b)   Made by Fraser & Chalmers Ltd, Erith, to RP specification.
(c)   ex ?
(d)   ex Buckminster quarries 8/1933
(e)   ex Holwell quarries 6/1945
(f)   ex Islip quarries 1947
(g)   ex Glendon quarries 1948
(h)   ex ?
(i)   ex Kettering quarries c 1962

(1)   at Carrol Spring Nos. 2 and 3 quarries. To Holwell Ironworks 3/1941
(2)   dismantled 9/1940. Scrap sold to W.J. Redden & Sons, Wellingborough 10/1940
(3)   used with RP 340. s/s
(4)   to Marple & Gillott Ltd for scrap c 1935
(5)   at No. 5 quarry from 1936. Scr 1940
(6)   to Buckminster quarries 1/1940
(7)   new to No. 5 quarry; to No. 6 quarry. To Harlaxton quarries c 1967
(8)   at No. 5 quarry. to Isham quarries, loan and return, 1944.
       to No. 6 quarry. To Market Overton quarries (?) 5/1968
(9)   to Wirksworth quarries, Derbyshire 5/1949
(10) purchased by Reg. Bates; Scr c 1967 by Hunt Bros of Burton Latimer
(11) at ironworks, unloading skips. s/s
(12) at No. 6 quarry; to ironworks, unloading skips. To Cranford quarries 1969

Wellingborough Quarries & Mines.   Locomotive 85, beautifully restored in original livery by the Irchester Narrow Gauge Railway Trust, outside the goods shed in Irchester station yard, on 19th October 1985. The Trust has now moved into the country park.   A.J. Cocklin

FINEDON PARK QUARRIES

Owners: Keeble & Jellett; R.E. Campbell from 1st October 1914: Ebbw Vale Steel, Iron & Coal Co Ltd from 9th November 1915.

When the blackband ironstone of South Wales became exhausted in the middle of the 19th century, several railway promoters sought to link up the area with the Northamptonshire orefields, but the only scheme that came to fruition was the Stratford upon Avon & Midland Junction Railway. The import of Spanish ore killed the prospects envisaged, but in the different economic conditions of the 20th century the South Wales ironmasters came to Northamptonshire to open their own quarries, of which the present example was the first.

Finedon Hall was the seat of the Mackworth Dolbens in its last period as a country residence, and in the late 19th century was in the ownership of Miss Ellen Mackworth Dolben, a lady well remembered for her kindness to local people. Her signature appeared on a number of ironstone leases to Wellingborough Iron Co Ltd, Walter Neilson and others, but she was the last of her line and on her death on 2nd February 1912 the estate of 250 acres was sold to George Keeble and Edward Henry Jellett; the estate was heavily mortgaged and had probably only been kept going for some time by ironstone royalties. Keeble was what would be described as a 'developer', and was associated with at least three areas in the ironstone country, including Finedon, Denford and Barrowden. Keeble himself bought the hall and grounds at the auction in June 1912, but resold the hall in August.

According to the *'Kettering Leader'* of 22nd November 1912, the promoters hoped to load 300 tons of ore per day. As the siding agreement with the Midland Railway and the permission from Finedon UDC to lay a tramway across Harrowden Road were both dated June 1913, production probably commenced later that year, in which it is so quoted by LQ; whereupon the owners proceeded to carry on where Walter Neilson had left off 26 years before (see under the Thingdon Quarries section) by felling more of the hall avenue to get the ore beneath. (*'Kettering Leader'*, 21st March 1913). In 1914 R.E. Campbell purchased the entire property (Denford included), only to sell it in the following year to the Ebbw Vale company.

The quarries were mainly on the southeastern fringe of Finedon Park, at the top of the hill, and another variety (for this district) of rail system was introduced to work them – a two-foot gauge tramway in the park to carry the ore in side-tipping wagons to a platform alongside a standard gauge line that made direct connection with the Midland Railway, and which was naturally steeply graded. The stone was not however taken away in one operation but was calcined at a point about half way along the standard gauge line, which was some three quarters of a mile in length. This must have involved an extra unloading operation, and it would have been simpler mechanically to calcine after tipping from the narrow gauge and then load the burnt ore on the standard gauge. Possibly the site was chosen so that the calcining operations should be carried on outside the park. There was also a recollection that the ore was taken down by gravity from the clamps to Wellingborough Sidings. About 1920 use was also made of Neilson's tunnel under Harrowden Road to work stone to the south. The pits were kept open during the war years of scarcity, but the ore was of poor quality, and the pits were closed in 1921 and the track dismantled save for a length in the Harrowden Road level crossing to preserve (so it was said) the right-of-way in the event of reopening, which occurred many years later.

Traction on the standard gauge portion was by steam locomotive, housed at the upper terminus; this was a standard Peckett 0-6-OST, one of several that had been used at Portland, and arrived one snowy winter's day – the driver's son having to fill the tank by bucket from a stream. There was a rumour that the locomotive was once impounded by the MR when she passed the gate on to railway property, and was not allowed back until the railway company's account had been settled. It was also rumoured that when Ebbw Vale took over, this engine had not been paid for! On the narrow gauge it was generally understood that ponies were used, and Mr L.J. Dunkley, probably in 1984 the only surviving quarryman, stated that this was so. However, for a short period LITTLE TICH (so named from its diminutive proportions) was borrowed from the cement works at Irthlingborough; this locomotive, though only an ironstone engine by proxy, as it were, is worthy of mention as being the only locomotive proper built by the Glasgow Railway Engineering Co Ltd, a venture started by Dugald Drummond between his periods of office on the Caledonian Railway and the LSWR.[1] Further, the 6ins OS shows a building that would seem to be a locomotive shed, suggesting loco. haulage on a regular rather than a temporary basis; and in 1984 Mr E.H. Amey produced a photograph taken in 'The Grove' (Finedon Park) of a small Orenstein & Koppel 0-4-OWT, apparently out of use. The young people on the footplate (his aunts and uncle) date the photograph to the 1913–15 period; the identity of the locomotive has not been discovered, and it might have been used by the contractors building the system. Frank Frost (Traffic Manager of Wellingborough Iron Co Ltd) remembers as a boy playing in the old quarry about 1921/2, when there were 'several old iron side tip wagons about'.

There are plenty of traces of the route still to be seen. At its lower (western) end, the standard gauge route was later incorporated into Richard Thomas's Finedon system (which see) but north of the level crossing with Harrowden Road the two routes diverge, the Finedon Park system lying to the south of the other. It was carried up the slope of the hill on a low embankment, still in position and now covered by trees and with one length of rail surviving; the site of the calcine bank is a rough scrubby area inhabited by muntjac (Chinese barking deer). Entering the park, the line curved towards the narrow gauge terminal; the area where the locomotive shed is marked on the OS carries no present indication of the building, but, where the line to it crossed a stream, the bridge abutments can be seen. The trans-shipment point where the narrow gauge paralleled the standard gauge is clearly observable, with the former embanked at this point but running eastward in a shallow cutting. Several half-buried pieces of rail are still here (1984) and appear to derive from both standard and narrow gauge lines, with the narrow gauge examples of the bullhead type.

The whole area is quite picturesque, embowered as it is with trees on all sides, through we presume it was a great deal more open when quarrying was in progress. The area between the spinney and Harrowden Road has been returned to agricultural use and ploughed up completely such that no traces of the tramway are apparent apart from one small cutting near the road. The quarry site at the eastern end of the park is indicated by ground sunk below road level but has now been built upon.

Footnotes

1.   J.B. Latham, *'The Railway Observer'* 1941, p 116.

Grid References

900704	Junction with MR
900710	Level crossing with Harrowden Lane

906714	Calcine banks (east end)
908714	s.g. locomotive shed
909714	n.g. locomotive shed
909715	Tipping dock to s.g.

Locomotives

Gauge; 4ft 8½ins

No. 9   0-6-OST   OC   P   751   1898 14 x 20ins   3ft 7ins   (a)   (1)

(a)   ex Hill & Co, contractors, Portland Bill, via J. Pugsley & Sons Ltd, Stoke Gifford.

(1)   to Ebbw Vale Ironworks c 1921

Gauge; 2ft 0ins

(unknown name)	0-4-OWT	OC	OK	(a)	s/s
LITTLE TICH	0-4-OST	OC	Glasgow Rly Eng Co 1897	(b)	(1)

(a)   ex ?
(b)   ex Premier Cement Co Ltd, Irthlingborough, loan

(1)   ret. to Premier Cement Co Ltd

Finedon Park Quarries. The 2ft gauge line was usually worked by horses, but a locomotive was borrowed from the Premier Cement works for a time. The OK locomotive in the photograph, taken at 'The Grove' in Finedon Park, is of unknown identity and origin; it may have been used to work the quarries, or by a contractor laying the track etc. The date is about 1914, judging from the age of Ted Amey's uncle and aunts on the footplate!

Collection E.H. Amey

FINEDON QUARRIES

Owners: Glendon Iron Co: Glendon Iron Co Ltd from 23rd June 1886: Charles Barlow from 1901: Harold Barlow from c 1920: Richard Thomas & Co Ltd from 3rd April 1936: Richard Thomas & Baldwins Ltd from 3rd January 1945.

Finedon quarries were operated in three separate and distinct phases with time lapses between them, by different companies with different policies and operating methods, and apart from the common site there was little physical association between the three. Under Glendon Iron Co ownership the pits supplied ore solely to feed Finedon furnaces; next, the quarries were worked as an independent unit by the Barlows, a prominent local family; and finally the area came into the orbit of Richard Thomas & Co Ltd as an extension of their Irthlingborough system. The thread linking them is the ownership of the land and leases, which were unusually complex, and which makes it desirable to describe them in one section.

In 1866 the Glendon Iron Co, which for a few years previously had been quarrying at Glendon, north of Kettering, commenced the manufacture of iron at their Finedon furnaces, which lay alongside the Midland Railway just south of Finedon station on the east side. At first, ore from Glendon was used but very shortly afterwards was supplemented by stone from the immediate vicinity, transported by standard gauge tramway operated by steam locomotives from the outcrop east of the Ise. This is confirmed by a reference in '*Mining Journal*' of 30th September, 1871, p. 861, to a line 'direct to the furnaces, a distance of about one mile', and the 1884 OS shows such a line extending to the vicinity of the windmill southeast of Mill Lane. The date of the first ironstone lease has not been discovered but presumably was granted by the Mackworth Dolbens of Finedon Hall. Leases to dig clay for bricks, also manufactured on the site, were granted in 1874/76/77. Two further leases were granted by Mrs Frances Mackworth Dolben and Miss Ellen Mackworth Dolben; the first, dated 25th March 1885 for 30 years, was for limestone over about 148 acres of ground, roughly half of each side of the Finedon–Burton Latimer road. The second, of 24th June 1888 for 26¾ years (i.e. to terminate concurrently with the previous lease) was for ironstone in two separate areas; Harlocks and Little Cossical (two fields totalling 21 acres) adjoining Station road on the east side near Mill Lane, and Eight Acres and Mill Orchard (two fields totalling 18 acres) bordering Holly Walk on the northwest corner of Finedon park. The plan attached to the lease shows projected tramway connections in the form of a branch to 'Eight Acres' and an extension along the northwest side of Mill Lane as far as Station Road. The 1901 OS shows evidence of quarrying for limestone in the area covered by the 1885 lease on the southwest side of Burton Road, and it is possible that the tramway to this crossed Station Road on the level and then through 'Harlocks'. In 1890, or possibly 1889, permission was received to tunnel beneath Station Road, but a report in the *'Wellingborough News'* of 25th April 1890 states that this was 'half completed', suggesting that it was not opened by the Glendon Iron Co Ltd, as they ceased operations in the following year.

Finedon furnaces were taken over by Islip Iron Co Ltd, who did not however reopen them, nor the quarries as far as is known, and the quarry tramway was lifted to a point about half way along Mill Lane (see 1901 OS); but J. Kidner and C.H. Plevins (in effect the Islip Iron Co) negotiated with Miss Mackworth Dolben a lease for 21 years from 25th March 1893, covering the former 1885 lease and extending to the Poplar Lodge area, 210 acres in all. Preserved in the surveyor's office at Corby is the ledger of private letters by John Kidner; from these we learn that in July 1900 the firm of Attenborough & Timms commenced negotiations with John Kidner, the Islip chairman, for a sub-lease for the remainder of the term, i.e. to 25th March 1914; they were only interested in the ironstone initially, but the sub-lease from 25th March 1901 covered limestone as well as ironstone. Attenborough & Timms did not however operate the quarries themselves but brought in Charles Barlow in the role of a contractor, in much the same way as they had employed Edward Coles to do the quarrying at their Spratton and Brixworth quarries, and 'Mr. Barlow' is mentioned as 'seeing the route' in a letter from John Kidner of 17th October 1900.

The *'Kettering Guardian'* of 6th March 1908 states that about 1899 Charles Barlow purchased some freehold land that he developed for ironstone extraction; the site is not quoted but very probably was the field to the northeast of the Station Road Cemetery (consecrated 17th November 1892),[1] so had already had an interest in the area. He was a prominent local character, owning a brickworks, a grocery and a farm; he was a J.P. and a leading Baptist in the area. Richard Timms was Deacon at College Street Baptist Church in Northampton and the business association between the two men might well have arisen through their religious contacts; in those days religious persuasions played a much greater part in everyday affairs than today. Richard Attenborough (who was Church of England, by the way) died in 1901. So there we have it – Attenborough & Timms holding the leases and probably marketing the ore, and Charles Barlow doing the hard work on the ground. Locally however the workings were always known as 'Barlow's Pits', as he was the man on the spot; and he is therefore the one of greater interest to us. In LQ the workings are attributed to Attenborough & Timms from 1902 until 1913, when the firm gave up their ironstone business (as described under Brixworth Quarries). From 1914 onwards the quarries appear under Barlow's name in LQ, but some of the leases were still not held by him (see below).

John Kidner had suggested a narrow gauge line from the quarries to the former brickworks area at the back of the furnaces, where the ore could be transferred via a tipping dock to the standard gauge system that Islip operated, but instead of this Barlow laid a 1ft 11½ins gauge tramway from the quarries to the top of Mill Lane, and the existing standard gauge line was extended to meet it by a set of four sidings. The one nearest Mill Lane was used mainly for wagons of coal brought up for Finedon gasworks, which collected it therefrom; the next two sidings lay each side of an elevated tipping dock served by two narrow gauge tracks, and the fourth was adjacent to calcine banks. There were three of these – one building, one burning and one loading (by plank and barrow into railway wagons); but some ore was sent away in the raw state from the tipping dock direct into wagons. The standard gauge section was worked for Barlow by the Islip Iron Co Ltd until they ceased selling slag, when Francis T. Wright took over the locomotive and shunting rights.

The furnaces, as already stated, were not relit, and the plant was dismantled in the early years of the century, apart from the chimney, not felled until 1923 (as reported in the *'Kettering Leader'* of 17th August 1923). An unexpected market was developed for the very large quantity of slag that had accumulated in Glendon days, and which was found to be useful as railway ballast. Two locomotives were sent from Islip to work this traffic, the original Glendon engines having been sent to Islip on the closure of the furnaces. Much of the slag went to the Great Central Railway and when work finally ceased in 1925, quarrying was going on below ground level, where the slag had sunk over the years; this information came from Mr R. Mackintosh of Francis T. Wright Ltd. The site was then taken over by Francis T. Wright Ltd, wagon builders, who

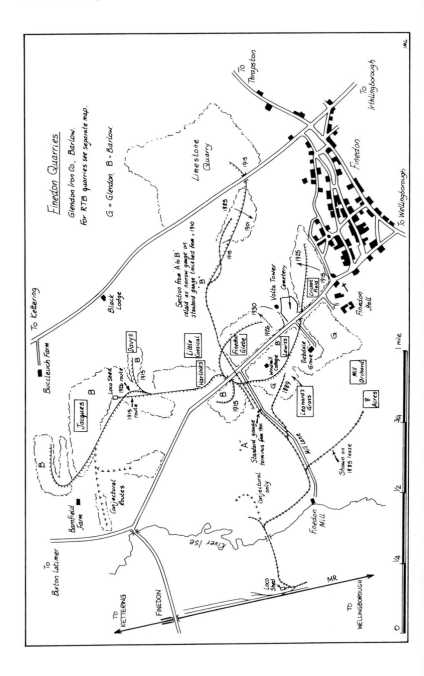

Finedon Quarries

Glendon Iron Co., Barlow.
For RTB quarries see separate map.

G = Glendon, B = Barlow.

ceased work here about 1960, and the Excelsior Patent Stone Co Ltd, promoted to use the slag in making a patent firebrick; but the latter was not a success because of the sulphur in the slag, and the premises were taken over by E. & S. Beddoes, who made kerb stones, paving slabs, etc. Of the two ex-Islip locomotives owned by Francis T. Wright Ltd, ISLIP NO. 2 was latterly plain black, but had been green originally; the livery of ISLIP No. 1 is unknown but was probably similar.

Returning to our consideration of the quarries, an extensive area to the east and south of Barnfield farm in Burton Latimer parish seems to have been worked first. The narrow gauge line utilized the tunnel built (or half-built!..) by Glendon Iron Co Ltd and ran north and northwest for a distance of nearly one mile, with branches to the working faces; the locomotive shed was rather remotely placed, about half way along, and was brick-built, with a smithy and a separate shed for stores, and a windpump for filling the water tank by the side of the shed, which had accommodation for three locomotives. The first came from W.G. Bagnall Ltd in September 1901, and two more followed in the next six years, plated C.B. No. 1, 2 and 3 respectively.

As was common among quarry systems of the day, the working faces took the names of the fields where they were situated, and these are sometimes quoted in LQ and GSM. Jacques pit, north of the locomotive shed, was operated up to about 1914 (certainly not afterwards, as the lease expired that year), while on the Finedon side of the boundary was a pit near Station Road and one near Davy's Lodge – the latter east of the main tramway and shown on a Richard Thomas plan as 'Davy's Quarry'. Barlow also reopened the limestone quarries, continuing the line under Burton Road via a tunnel. The ironstone pits were all becoming exhausted and from 1912 most of the quarrying was in the vicinity of Finedon, where Charles Barlow is recorded (by the *'Kettering Leader'* of 15th November 1912) as working the recreation and council fields on the north side of Avenue Road, alongside which permission was given to demolish certain buildings. The ground leased from the local council. Barlow was also working his own piece of ground adjoining – called the Cricket Field pit, the Finedon Cricket Club doubtless having to play elsewhere the while – and to the north of this was Finedon Glebe, which had been leased to Wellingborough Iron Co Ltd but which was worked for them by Barlow in 1913/4; a letter from Charles Barlow to Wellingborough Iron Co Ltd, dated 3rd March 1913, states that Barlow agreed to remove the ironstone over twelve months. The glebe land was

Finedon Quarries. There were three phases of operation of these quarries, the most interesting being the middle one when the quarries were served by a 2ft gauge tramway operated by Charles Barlow, and later by his son Harold. Three Bagnall locomotives provided the motive power, and shown here are C.B. No. 1 (left) and C.B. No. 2 (right) about 1928.

Fred Whitehead; Collection R.M. Smith

served by a tramway branch leaving the locomotive shed line by the bridge under Station Road, but to reach the quarries on the south side of the cemetery (tunneling beneath which was ruled out!) a new bridge was laid from the southern terminus of the narrow gauge and taken under Station Road by a skew bridge; it passed en route through Leonard's Grass, that had been worked by the Glendon Iron Co some thirty years before, and the opportunity was taken to remove the small amount of stone remaining. This pit, opened up by the Lewis brothers, was also known to the men as 'Lewis's Pit'.

Attenborough & Timms relinquished their ironstone business in 1913 and LQ quotes Charles Barlow as the quarry owner in the following year. Attenborough had died in 1901 and Timms now proposed to retire. Barlow is also reported, in the board minutes of the Islip Iron Co Ltd of 25th January 1913, to have bought a considerable area of ironstone and limestone land and as proposing to expand the business. The sublease with Kidner and Plevins was due to expire 25th March 1914 and these properties were purchased by the Ebbw Vale Steel, Iron & Coal Co Ltd 12th September 1917 along with many others (see Irthlingborough section). From 1914 onwards Barlow's operations were confined to the Finedon area, on ground owned or leased by him. The eastern end of the tramway near Avenue Road was in a gullet some thirty feet deep, and a pumping engine was installed to deal with water.

During the war and in other times when demand was high, all three narrow gauge locomotives were in daily use, with two locomotives on the standard gauge; but in the leaner years of the 'twenties, two narrow gauge and one standard gauge sufficed. When C.B. No. 3 required a new boiler, she was relegated to the back of the shed and cannibalised for spares. By 1920 all the working faces were clustered round Finedon Cemetery, and the tramway towards Burton Latimer unused for production. In the closing years of operation it was the practice to keep one locomotive (the oldest one, now sporting the name DEVIL) in the nearby tunnel, an arrangement that suited the driver, who lived in Finedon, saving him a fair walk to and from work; the old shed was reached by footpath from Burton Latimer. Whether at this time there were two narrow gauge locomotives in use, or only one, is uncertain.

Most of the land was then owned by Ebbw Vale Steel Iron & Coal Co Ltd as part of their Irthlingborough development and they leased 7¾ acres near the cemetery to Barlow for nine years from 14th June 1919. All the area was collectively referred to as Cricket Field pit, which was worked intensively during World War I; but the cricket field proper was regrassed and sold to the cricket club by 1920.[2] Charles Barlow was succeeded as quarry manager by his son Harold, recorded in this capacity by '*Kelly's Directory*' in 1920 but not until 1925 by LQ, and he carried on the business until the end. Charles Barlow died 5th January 1923. Barlow's brickworks in School Lane, incidentally, was a small affair that never used locomotives, and was closed sometime about the beginning of World War I, the pit being used as a rubbish tip by the local authority. Operations in the Cricket Field area seem to have ceased with the sale of the remaining land to Ebbw Vale 3rd October 1925, but work continued in the Glebe site, with new faces Volta Tower and Stable Field, dating from 1920; the Glebe area was leased from Wellingborough Iron Co Ltd to Harold Barlow for seven years from 25th March 1924.

For details of the tramway and quarry equipment we are indebted to information recorded by Mr R.M. Smith, who as a boy in the early 1930's spent most of his summer holidays at the quarries, writing down what he saw of operations then and what he learnt from Fred Whitehead, the engine driver; his detailed description of everyday things is a most valuable contemporary record. The locomotives were standard Bagnall machines of the same design, but as new No. 2 had slightly smaller wheels; however, Mr. Whitehead said that No. 3 was the one with smaller wheels, indicating some exchanges. As locomotive maintenance was carried out by the locomotive crews themselves, he should know: this work, including even boiler exchanging, was carried out at weekends, often overnight. Once, an outside firm was called in to reprofile the tyres of one engine, which they did to a square instead of tapered section, with disastrous results in derailments and cutting off boltheads at points. The experiment was not repeated!

Wagons were steel V-shaped side-tippers holding about one ton of ore, and were maintained by the blacksmith. Three wagons would be left at the working face overnight for the men (who started work at 6.00am) to fill. Meanwhile at the loco. shed the locomotives would be getting up steam and by 8.00am the pair of them would double-head the empties to the pit, leave them in a loop and then run into the pit to collect the wagons filled the previous day. There was a fair gradient out of the Cricket Field pit and No. 1 and No. 2 made a fine sight, blasting out of the pit with thirty wagons in tow and under the long skew bridge, with sparks bouncing off the roof. The train was taken to Mill Lane Sidings and reversed on to the cally bank or tipping dock as required. Trains from the

Volta Tower pit did not have to reverse and the locomotive moved to the rear of the train by some 'fly-shunting' at the loop, i.e. the loco. would be uncoupled by the 'rope-runner' and accelerate over the points, which the roperunner would then alter for the train. Locomotives worked chimney first out of the quarries. Track on both narrow and standard gauges was flat-bottomed attached to wooden sleepers by steel 'dogs' (so-called from the shape of the heads); at the cally banks however sections of track permanently attached to steel sleepers facilitated the continual slewing required as the bank was built up.

The standard gauge equipment was in poor shape by the 1920's; the track, with bridges over the Ise and a stream and two sharp bends, probably dated from Glendon days, and the locomotives supplied by Islip were of comparable vintage. ISLIP No. 1 was cut up when requiring heavy overhaul, but ISLIP No. 2 soldiered on; she was originally painted bright green, but this darkened with age and polishing and she finished up plain black. With her semicircular smokebox door, narrow weatherboard and tall chimney, she looked her years but worked well nevertheless, chuffing about the yard and snorting up the hill. Wagons were wooden, lettered 'C. Barlow', or sometimes hoppers for ironworks who supplied their own wagons.

Finedon Quarries. No. 20 steam shovel, RH 535, evidently used for removing overburden, about 1928. Note the ironstone face at the foot of the picture, and narrow gauge side-tipping wagon at left.

Fred Whitehead;
Collection R.M. Smith

137

Finedon Quarries. Taylor & Hubbard steam crane, about 1938. This is the only known example by this maker in the ironstone fields. Collection R.M. Smith

In Charles Barlow's day, the quarries were excavated by the familiar 'plank and barrow' method, but in 1919, to cope with increasing overburden in Cricket Field pit, a Ruston 'steam crane navvy' was purchased; she came in pieces and was assembled in the pit, starting work in June 1920. The local populace came along to see 'the American Devil' (as these machines were often termed) and it became a nine-days wonder; she was later transferred to the Volta Tower pit. There was also another steam navvy and a Taylor & Hubbard steam crane.

Working conditions were hard, as everywhere in the industry. During the war 200 men were employed, when 1000 tons a day were despatched. 'Strippers' were paid per square yard of topsoil removed; 'muck shifters' removed overburden, about 12 cubic yards per day; 'rock fillers' loaded 16 wagons of ore per day, being paid 4¼d a ton; 'cally' fillers took calcined

Finedon Quarries. When Barlows ceased work in 1930, there was a considerable stockpile of calcined ore on the banks alongside Mill Lane, and this was removed in the middle 1930s, using the standard gauge locomotive ISLIP No. 2, loaned by Francis T. Wright Ltd. As a lad, Bob Smith spent much of his summer holidays watching her at work, and kindly loaned us this photograph. Standing by the engine is the quarry manager and his son, presumably the driver.   Collection R.M. Smith

Finedon Quarries. When Richard Thomas & Co. Ltd. acquired the Finedon site, they decided to reopen the quarries on a much bigger scale, with a standard gauge tramway system. For the preliminary work of clearing the ground and installing equipment for taking the ore underground to the Irthlingborough plant, RT used a 3ft 8in gauge system with a locomotive, rails and wagons from the Hunsbury Hill site. The locomotive, which had seen little use at Hunsbury Hill, was WOOTTON, WB 1956, shown here on 16th April 1938.   G. Alliez/Courtesy B.D. Stoyel

ore, three hundredweights at a time, by barrow to railway wagons, and received ½d per barrow. Working hours were 6.00am to 4.00pm.

When quarrying ceased about September 1930, the narrow gauge track was dismantled and the locomotives were sold for scrap, but two calcine banks, each of about 30,000 tons, had been left standing and (possibly not immediately) these were dug away and sent to Shelton and other ironworks. This lasted until 1935, using ISLIP No. 2. The work – hard, poorly paid and very dirty, such that at the end of the day every man was covered in reddish-brown dust – was eagerly sought after in this time of heavy unemployment. Francis T. Wright Ltd took up the standard gauge layout beyond an unsafe bridge (over the Ise?). The quarries were left more or less as they were and were not restored. The Finedon Glebe area of 44 acres, including ironstone unworked by Barlow, was leased by Wellingborough Iron Co Ltd to Richard Thomas & Co Ltd for 25 years from 29th September 1937. The adjoining land to the east was owned by Ebbw Vale, the whole of whose properties in Finedon and Irthlingborough were made over to Richard Thomas 3rd April 1936. The Irthlingborough mines are dealt with separately, though the whole complex was regarded as one unit by Richard Thomas, as indeed had Ebbw Vale before them; but trading conditions, that had generally been poor during Ebbw Vale's tenure, were now much improved and Richard Thomas vigorously developed both mine and quarry properties, with the intention of dealing with the output from both at the Irthlingborough plant.

On 8th June 1937 Richard Thomas held a meeting with the consulting engineering firm of H.A. Brassert & Co. to discuss the development of the Finedon site, described as the 'Buccleuch Area' and comprising two quarries, Ebbw Vale and Barlow's (respectively the former Cricket Field and Glebe quarries). It was hoped to be in full production by the following May, but as the heavy quarry machines required would not be available until about September, temporary plant would be used, that could afterwards be transferred to Hunsbury Hill to reopen the quarries there.

A north-south working face was driven north from the old Cricket Field pit in the general direction of Buccleuch Farm, which gave its name to the opencast quarry, and it was intended to lay track along this gullet so that ore could be tipped via a crusher into 3ft gauge wagons running underground from a new tunnel outlet to Irthlingborough. This project involved the shifting of a considerable volume of earth, and the top section of the new gullet was removed over a temporary tramway of 3ft 8ins gauge, the equipment – rails, side-tipping wagons and one locomotive – being brought over from the disused Hunsbury Hill system in 1937 and stacked in Barlow's quarry near the Volta Tower, along with a new 21RB diesel shovel.

A 20-ton steam navvy (not Barlow's) was used, so probably Barlow's machine had already gone, along with the locomotives; but the Taylor &

Finedon Quarries. A bit of a mystery picture this, dated about 1938. The deep quarry at the back is Buccleuch, identified by the barn. The shovel and narrow gauge tub in the foreground presumably date from Barlow's earlier operations, but the 20-ton machine, which was used by Richard Thomas & Co Ltd, remains unidentified. Collection E.H. Amey

Finedon Quarries. A temporary 3ft 8in gauge tramway was laid to assist in removing spoil etc. The track, locomotive and wagons were all brought in from the long-closed Hunsbury Hill site, which Richard Thomas had acquired about the same time as Finedon/Irthlingborough. 21RB shovel in the pit.   Mr. Gimber. Collection E.H. Amey

Hubbard crane was still present. The 'temporary plant' referred to in the previous paragraph mentions a 'steam transporter and a diesel digger' but we have been unable to confirm the presence of the former. The 21RB was 'moved from Barlow's quarry to Ebbw Vale quarry 8th September 1938', according to W.E. Davies' weekly reports in the Richard Thomas files, followed by the building on site of a 5360 Stripping Shovel and of a 4140 Loading Shovel. The first locomotive, WHISTON, came from Hunsbury Hill on April Fool's Day, 1939, and loading of stone commenced 15th May 1939, from behind the Volta Tower. The quarry was extended northwards in the direction of Buccleuch Farm, using the two shovels, then working from west to east under increasing cover. The quarry line was nearly a mile in length from the working face to the old Cricket Field Pit, where there was a reversing junction; a number of steel side-tipping wagons were pulled from the quarry and then pushed along a ledge of level ground alongside the 3ft line that emerged from the tunnel into Barlow's old gullet about thirty feet below. Between the two was a massive concrete wall that held a steel loading bunker, and alongside a tower of corrugated iron that housed the crusher. The ore was tipped from the wagons into the crusher, from which a conveyor belt fed the crushed ore into the bunker for loading the narrow gauge wagons. The tunnel from Irthlingborough, driven through from both ends, 'holed through' (with only six inches misalignment between the two alignments) on the night of Sunday 19th February 1939, as recorded by Mr D.S. Ferguson, the surveyor, in his diary – saved by Mr A.J. Pack, his successor. In the autumn of 1939 a chute was installed so that raw stone could be loaded directly into wagons, avoiding the crusher and screening plant. By June 1940 output was around 6000 tons per week, much the same as from the mines.

Beyond the tipping arrangements, but on an adjacent siding, was a single-road brick engine shed for two locomotives, but extended rearwards by 30ft 9ins in 1941 to hold three, with nearby on brick pillars a water tank from which a pipe led through the shed wall. Three Andrew Barclay locomotives, exhibiting a nice variety of painting styles and names, provided the motive power; WHISTON was plain black with red coupling rods and with the name in yellow letters, NEPTUNE brown, lined black edged yellow and with cast brass nameplates, and FINEDON dark green, lined black edged white, with the name in Barclay's standard transfers of gold with red and black shading.

The wagons were 'dumpcars', six of which were supplied by the Gloucester Railway Carriage & Wagon Co Ltd in 1941 (maker's numbers 22–27, so among the very first they had built); but the few dumpcars that survived the closure were built by Metro-Cammell and were of more massive proportions and with reinforced sides. The 'Gloucesters' had a capacity of 10 cubic yards. The whole tramway was very substantially built, as seemed characteristic of Richard Thomas & Co Ltd, though as a wartime emergency project it qualified for Government assistance.

The locomotive shed was in the shadow of the Volta Tower, a prominent local landmark built to the memory of a member of the Dolben family of Finedon Hall, lost off the African coast in the S.S. VOLTA. The tower was dismantled in the middle 1950's, following a partial collapse on 16th November 1951, when one of the occupants was killed. It was thought that deep quarrying very close to the tower had disturbed the foundations, but it was said that the tower had been built without mortar, a factor hardly likely to enhance its stability (see *Finedon otherwise Thingdon*; John L.H. Bailey, 1975).

The arrangement involving transfer from standard to narrow gauge (instead of the more usual reverse) was not used for very long on its own, as in 1941 the quarry was linked by a direct line to the LMSR at

Finedon Quarries. The standard gauge tramway under construction, with a presumed 10RB diesel digger at work. Narrow gauge lines are in the cutting in the foreground, 1938. Note the Volta Tower, which collapsed in November 1951.

Mr. Gimber. Collection E.H. Amey

Finedon Quarries. The crusher under construction, in front of the concrete stage from which the ore was to be discharged from standard gauge wagons. Note narrow gauge wagons full of spoil at the foot of the picture. 1938. Mr. Gimber. Collection E.H. Amey

Finedon Quarries. The tunnel to Irthlingborough being driven through the face of Barlow's old quarry. In attendance is a Ruston locomotive (centre) and a small digger (right). Note that the tunnel is not at the end of the quarry, but offset to the side. 1938.

Mr. Gimber. Collection E.H. Amey

Finedon Quarries. No photographs of the three Andrew Barclay locomotives on site have been discovered. Shown here is the former NEPTUNE, photographed at RTB's Elba Works, Gowerton on 3rd June 1960.

R.S. Fraser

Wellingborough. The line left the sidings there at the north end – protected by a board stating 'No movement to be made past this board without the permission of the signalman at Neilson (sic) Siding Box' – and, after passing a gate, divided into four sidings that reunited short of the crossing with Harrowden Road (or Lane), where there was a weighbridge and loop. The sidings had wooden sleepers and LNWR chairs. The line thus far was very nearly on the course of the former Finedon Park tramway, but crossed the Ise by a concrete instead of a wooden bridge, and beyond the level crossing ascended the hill slightly to the north at a steep gradient, reaching the summit in deep cutting and passing beneath Station Road by a bridge of blue brick, to join the existing quarry line via a gap in the old Cricket Field working face. The cutting destroyed two thirds of Holly Walk, a famous Finedon estate landmark for over two centuries. Calcine clamps were established on the lower slopes of the hill north of the level crossing, and from here up the hill the track was ballasted and laid on wooden sleepers lower down the hill and concrete sleepers in the cutting. Flat-bottomed track in 40-foot lengths, 75 lbs per yard, was used in the sidings and in the quarry, bullhead rail in 60-foot lengths on the heavier duty line.

Permission for the bridge under Station Road was granted by Wellingborough UDC on 11th March 1941 and construction evidently commenced immediately, as a 490 'grab' was sent to Harrowden Lane to operate the calcine clamps in June 1941. Most of the traffic from Buccleuch quarry was then routed this way, but not all of it; a small amount continued to go out via the tunnel up to about 1945. Two more quarry machines were acquired – a 24RB for work at Harrowden Lane clamps, and a 37RB in the quarry on loading duties. The quarry was however essentially a wartime feature and after the war it did not last long, being closed on 23rd May 1946; RTB were planning to restart operations by quarrying and mining (north of Burton Road) up to 1954, but nothing came of this. There was no hurry to dismantle the effects however, particularly the main railway, which remained in situ for nearly twenty years, when it was lifted as part of the general closure at Irthlingborough. The quarry machines and locomotives were disposed of one by one; the crusher was dismantled in the summer of 1949, while the rest of the plant was taken down and disappeared piecemeal in the late 1950's and the 1960's.

There was a considerable mound of calcined ore left in the clamps by Harrowden Lane and some of this was removed in the very early 1950's;

as all the locomotives had gone, a former Lancashire & Yorkshire 0-4-0ST, 51217, was hired from BR, being handed over at the demarcation point between BR and RTB property on Monday mornings and returned on Friday afternoons, returning to Wellingborough shed for washout, etc. It was said that it was not left in the open overnight, so presumably went up the bank to the RTB loco. shed. Though this exercise is well authenticated by both BR and RTB personnel, the actual period has eluded research; BR has no official record of the loan of the locomotive, even to Wellingborough, let alone to RTB, but she moved from Burton shed to Bath in February 1953, and is unlikely to have been loaned from the latter. Local recollection favours 1951/2. Another locomotive of this class, 51235, was hired a year or so later to help move the 5360 machine in pieces down to BR for transit to Blisworth.

Track in the quarry and shed yard were lifted around 1960, and odd pieces had gone before that, but the rest of the main line remained in position; it quickly became less and less easily passable, as saplings pushing their way between the concrete sleepers on the bank grew into trees. Other changes in the 1950's included the smoothing over of Barlow's old workings north of Station Road (to the regret of botanists at

Finedon Quarries. Jib of the 5360 stripping shovel awaiting transport to Blisworth, about 1954. It is in the sidings approaching the BR marshalling yard at Wellingborough.

Collection E.H. Amey

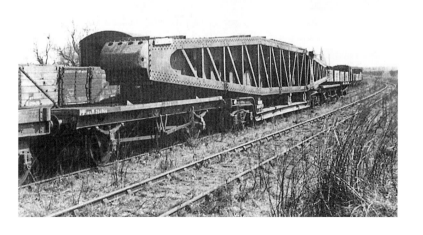

the loss of a number of rare plants), and replacing the former hedges by wire fences. In 1959 there still remained in a field near the Volta Tower two wooden wagons from Hunsbury Hill, both in derelict condition but of different capacity – 32 and 85 cubic feet; they were taken away for scrap a year or so later. While on the subject of narrow gauge wagons, a small wooden side-tipper was noted by Sydney Leleux in the Cricket Field area in 1964; the body was 6ft wide, 3ft 3ins long and 1ft 5ins high, on a frame 5ft 3ins long – probably also from Hunsbury Hill.

Steps to lift the main track took place late in 1965, when the bushes growing on the reception sidings just outside the BR boundary were cleared, and four dumpcars that had stood on the weighbridge loop were cut up in November. The heavy growth on the line up the hillside was also cleared, so that the yellow Nordberg Trackshifter loaned by Irchester could get up to the quarry (a few lengths of rail had to be reinstated to do this) and start lifting the track; this was at the beginning of 1966 and the job was completed by the beginning of July. Each length of rail was pulled down by the trackshifter to be stacked by the Harrowden Lane level crossing; in all 265 lengths of flat-bottom rail and well over 300 of bullhead, the former going to Blisworth quarries and the latter for scrap. The line to BR west of the occupation bridge was left in situ, until January 1985, when the embankment was levelled.

There are still a number of remains of the Finedon system. The focal point for the Barlow remains is the tunnel under Station Road, a few yards northwest of Mill Lane; the parapets remain, of red brick with a sector of concrete capping on the northeast side of the road, a rectangular capping on the southwest side, on which side the bridge is still open (though obscured by elder bushes) underneath to reveal a rather intricate 'dog tooth' arrangement of layers of brick, which were repointed in 1978; the other side is filled in, but a shallow depression across the fields shows the direction of the route, past a replacement hedge and overland to the ruinous locomotive shed. The whole edifice is on a low mound, the ground in the vicinity having been quarried. In 1968 the rear wall, complete with three window frames, was largely intact, but invaded by bushes (mostly elder) that have continued their relentless pressure so that by 1977 most of the brickwork had fallen in, as had the stores at the rear. The pit is visible, and at the side is a cylindrical water tank on brick supports that have been repointed, and the tank is evidently in use; the windpump, the vanes of which were on the ground in 1977, had been restored to use by 1983. Further up towards Burton Latimer is

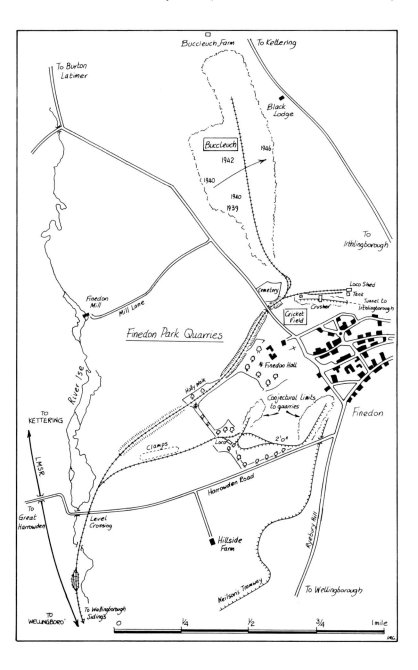

Finedon Quarries. The standard gauge tramway near the summit of the deep cutting through Holly Walk, looking towards the bridge under Station Road, 3rd November 1962.

S.A. Leleux

Finedon Quarries. 3ft 8ins gauge wagon body from Hunsbury Hill, still on site 11th April 1964. S.A. Leleux

Finedon Quarries.   At the close of operations, the dumpcars were collected in the sidings close to the BR yard, and remained there for twenty years before being cut up in November 1965. They are of Metro-Cammell design. 21st September 1965.   M.J. Leah

Finedon Quarries.   Tunnel under Station Road, just west of Mill Lane. The bridge is still there but has been encroached upon by bushes and ivy a good deal more. 24th March 1977.
Eric Tonks

a long terminal gullet marking the site of a quarry branch shown on the 1905 OS, but in 1983 the bushes in it had been cut down as a step towards restoration. A remnant of Davy's quarry can be seen from the loco. shed site, looking towards Buccleuch quarry; and there are two small relics by the roadside – a one-time gullet now planted with trees, and a low embankment, respectively east and west of the road junction. The latter, opposite Burton mill, may be a relic from early days, when the Glendon Iron Co. were operating Finedon furnaces; Gerald Farrow was told as a boy that it was the site of a horse-worked tramway that ran from a quarry north of Barnfield farm to a roadside loading deck, whence the ore was taken by horse and cart to the furnaces.

If we retrace our steps to Mill Lane, a pleasant backwater, still with its mill, a few more traces can be made out. There is a copse of pines at the corner where Mill Lane joins Station Road, and at its western tip a mound of earth that suggests the narrow gauge was elevated here to permit the use of side-tippers. Below this point and between Mill Lane and the stream chuckling along the eastern side is an embankment that accords with the route shown on the 1884 OS. Back on the northwestern side of Mill Lane below the next bend a deposit of slag ballast indicates the route of the standard gauge line dating from Glendon days, and the course of this can be followed by the side of the spinney alongside the Ise up to the site of the bridge over the latter; the ballast on the spinney section is ash. The standard gauge locomotive shed, losing slates and apparently in danger of falling down, was still in position in 1983, and can be seen from passing trains. Along Station Road, between Mill Lane corner and Finedon Hall (now in ruins) the low fields on each side reveal the extraction of ore, but there are no other traces, and further east a smoothed-over hump of ground crossed by wire fences marks the beginning of Buccleuch Quarry. The narrow gauge passed under Station Road by a very skew bridge near the entrance to Debdale, and the site of the bridge is marked by an ivy-clad parapet on the southwest side of the road, and some ten feet below it is the red brick tunnel arch; the ironstone face is visible alongside and it is presumed that this is where DEVIL was latterly shedded. The bridge has been filled in on the northeast side, and there is no sign of the one-time tunnel beneath the drive to Debdale. One of the last quarries worked by Barlow was the Cricket Field pit, to which we have alluded several times; this was utilized by Richard Thomas in the opening of Buccleuch Quarry, and some of the faces remaining date from Barlow's day. It is still a cricket field, too! Of

Finedon Quarries. Narrow gauge locomotive shed from Barlow's occupation of the site, showing the windpump, water tank, and remains of the workshop, with the loco. shed behind. January 1968. Most of the brickwork has now fallen down but the windpump and water tank remain.   G.H. Starmer

Finedon Quarries. A party of IRS members inspect the old tramway route to Wellingborough sidings, on 23rd April 1988. This area has been taken over by the local council and is designated a Nature Trail, but its origin as a former tramway route is not in any doubt! This cutting cut through the noted Holly Walk of Finedon Hall.   A.J. Cocklin

the bridge under Burton Road only the parapet on the south side remains, of red brick capped with concrete with tetrahedra at the ends; sunken fields lie to the south and a bushy gullet, but nothing can be seen on the north side where the limestone quarries lay.

There are more obvious reminders of the rail system serving Buccleuch quarry. All the track has gone, but the route is clear most of the way from the BR yard at Wellingborough, including the bridge over the Ise and the level crossing of Harrowden Road, north of which sections of the old calcine banks can be seen. Beyond the banks the route crosses a stream by a concrete bridge, goes through a thicket and then curves to the northeast on a rising embankment, breached at one point for field access. The embankment is heavily overgrown with bushes throughout, passable here and there and carpeted with violets in the Spring. Higher up the hillside this gives way to a cutting of increasing depth, where trees predominate and it is easy to thread a way through the very pleasant glade. All the sleepers seem to have been left, wood on the embankment, concrete on the gradient in the cutting, wood again on the level top section; near the top bank on the south side the cutting is wider, possibly for storage sidings that were never laid. At the summit is the bridge under Station Road, of blue brick with plain flat concrete tops; the cutting here was used as a tip for miscellaneous refuse, and the bridge walls are covered with graffiti, but the rubbish was removed when the trackbed was converted into a 'Nature Trail' (see below). The smoke-blackening of the tunnel roof bears witness to the hard work the locomotives were required to do. By the side of the bridge is a planked route used by the contractor's plant in opening up the site. Beyond the bridge the courses of the standard and narrow gauge lines are still clear, and the most spectacular concrete wall where the wagons used to tip their loads into the bunker; this is used by amateur rock-climbers as a practice area but is now (1987) fenced off for safety. The locomotive shed and nearby water tank on its brick piers were left, but suffered badly from vandalism, particularly in the 1980's; but it was still possible to see where the 1941 extension joined the original building. The shed and water tank were demolished early in 1987. The old mine entrance at the lower level has been bricked up like its counterpart at Irthlingborough, and it is interesting to note that it is not at the end of the cutting but offset to the north; this is because the cutting, made by Barlow, whilst not exactly in line with Richard Thomas's proposed tunnel, was near enough so to be used. Traces of Barlow's pumping house can be seen on the south side,

Finedon Quarries. The bridge that formerly took the line under Station Road on its way to Wellingborough sidings. It now forms an access point to the Nature Trail. 23rd March 1985.
A.J. Cocklin

Finedon Quarries. Output destined for Irthlingborough was tipped from standard gauge dumpcars to the 3ft line at the lower level via a chute or crusher. The impressive concrete foundations of this equipment form a very solid reminder. The narrow gauge tramway ran where the bushes are, below; the standard gauge route is now fenced off for safety, as the area is open to public access. 23rd April 1988.   A.J. Cocklin

Finedon Quarries. The standard gauge shed for three locomotives, and water tower, at the end of the sidings, 10th September 1969. It is surprising that this lasted so long, but eventually decay and vandalism led to its being demolished in 1987.   M.J. Leah

Finedon Quarries. The bricked-up tunnel leading to Irthlingborough. Ruston & Hornsby diesel locomotives hauled trainloads of ore through this to the plant. This tunnel mouth was at one time very difficult of access but the removal of some trees has made this easier. 23rd April 1988.   A.J. Cocklin

and west of the concrete wall the steel base of the crusher.

Though the earlier working area has been smoothed over and returned to agriculture, much of the final gullet of Buccleuch quarry remains, straggling for about three quarters of a mile towards Black Lodge. The terminus of the pit by Buccleuch Farm was filled with rubbish under the euphemism of 'Burton Latimer Infill Site' and restored to agriculture, utilitarian and featureless. In 1983 the unrestored portion was donated by the British Steel Corporation Pension Fund to Wellingborough council for development mainly for public access, and early in 1984 clearance of saplings along the trackbed began. Councillor Bailey, who deplored the effects of the quarriers on the local scene, agreed that the area is now a haven for wildlife and flowers, and the railway cutting below the road bridge is now an attractive nature trail.

Footnotes

1. John L.H. Bailey, *Finedon otherwise Thingdon*, p. 136. Published by the author 1975.
2. John L. Bailey, *Finedon otherwise Thingdon*.

Grid References

Glendon Tramway

895724	Junction with MR
904723	Mill Lane level crossing
910723	Terminus of line

Barlow's Tramway

906733	Locomotive shed
907726	Bridge under Station Road (north)
910722	Bridge under Station Road (south)
906725	Tipping dock to s.g. line
901738	Tramway terminus (north end)
911724	Volta Tower
911722	Cricket Field (NW corner)
918725	Bridge under main road, for limestone quarries

RTB Quarries

900704	Junction with LMSR
900709	Bridge over Ise
900710	Level crossing with Harrowden Lane
911722	Bridge under Station Road
913723	Junction of line to Buccleuch Quarry

907737	North terminus of Buccleuch Quarry
915722	Tipping dock to n.g.
916722	n.g.tunnel mouth
916723	Locomotive shed

Locomotives

First Period, 1866–91 (Glendon Iron Co Ltd)

Gauge; 4ft 8½ins

3	EMILY	0-4-OST OC	HCR	163	1875	10 x 16ins	2ft 9ins	New 8/1875	s/s
4	FINEDON	0-4-OST OC	HCR	165	1876	13 x 20ins	3ft 6ins	New 2/1876	(1)
	FLORENCE	0-4-OST OC	MW	745	1879	12 x 18ins	3ft 0ins	New 5/1880	(1)
		0-4-OST OC	FE	184	1889				(2)

(1)   to Islip Iron Co Ltd
(2)   to Plevins & Co, Twywell Brickworks, c 1892

Also other locomotives, details unknown.

Second Period, 1901–35 (Charles & Harold Barlow)

Gauge; 1ft 11½ins

C.B. No. 1 DEVIL	0-4-OST OC	WB	1643	1901	6 x 9ins	1ft 7ins	New 9/1901	(1)
C.B. No. 2	0-4-OST OC	WB	1662	1902	6 x 9ins	1ft 6⅞ins	New 9/1902	(1)
C.B. No. 3	0-4-OST OC	WB	1802	1906	6 x 9ins	1ft 7ins	New 12/1906	(1)

(1)   W.J. Redden & Sons Ltd, Wellingborough (?) for scrap

Gauge; 4ft 8½ins (Operated by Islip Iron Co Ltd and later by Francis T. Wright Ltd)

ISLIP No. 1	0-4-OST OC	HE	138	1875	10 x 15ins	2ft 9ins	(a)	Scr c 1930
ISLIP No. 2	0-4-OST OC	HE	201	1878	10 x 15ins	2ft 9ins	(a)	Scr 1951

(a)   ex Islip Ironworks.

Third Period, 1937–47 (Richard Thomas & Baldwins Ltd)

Gauge; 3ft 8ins (Constructional line)

WOOTTON	0-6-OST OC	WB	1956	1912	13 x 18ins	2ft 9¼ins	(a)	s/s 1947

(a)   ex Hunsbury Hill Quarries 1937

Gauge; 4ft 8½ins

WHISTON	0-4-OST OC	AB	1333	1914	14 x 22ins	3ft 3ins	(a)	(1)

NEPTUNE	0-4-OST OC AB	1361	1913	14 x 22ins	3ft 3ins	(b)		(2)
FINEDON	0-4-OST OC AB	2129	1941	14 x 22ins	3ft 5ins	New 11/1942		(3)
No. 6	0-4-OST OC HCR	180	1876	13 x 20ins	3ft 3ins	(c)		(4)

(a)   ex Hunsbury Furnaces, 4/1939
(b)   ex New Westbury Iron Co Ltd, 7/1939
(c)   ex Wellingborough Iron Co Ltd, loan, 1941

(1)   to Landore Steelworks, 4/1951
(2)   to Elba Steelworks, Gowerton, 8/1950
(3)   to W. Gilbertson & Co Ltd, Pontardawe, 2/1956
(4)   returned to Wellingborough Iron Co Ltd 1941

Quarry Machines

Second Period, 1901–35 (Charles and Harold Barlow)

No. 20	S.Navvy	RH	535	1919	2¼ Cu.Yds.	31ft.	New 2/1919	
							s/s by 1937	
	S.Navvy	?					s/s	
	S.Crane	Taylor & Hubbard						(1)

(1) used by Richard Thomas & Co Ltd in opening up Buccleuch Quarry, 1937–8. s/s

Third Period, 1937–47 (Richard Thomas & Baldwins Ltd)

20 ton	S.Navvy	?						s/s
21RB	D.Shovel	RB	3639	1937	¾ Cu.Yds.	18ft 6ins	New 11/1937	(1)
10RB	D.Navvy	RB						(2)
5360	E.Stripping Shovel	R&R	669	1937	9 Cu.Yds.	104ft	(a)	(3)
4140	E.Shovel	R&R	670	1937	3½ Cu.Yds.	34ft	(b)	(4)
490	E. Grab/crane	R&R	1256	1941	2½ Cu.Yds.	36ft	New 1941	(5)
10RB	D.Shovel	RB	7676	1943			New 3/1943	(6)
37RB	D.Shovel	RB	7677	1943			New 5/1943	(7)
24RB	D.Shovel	RB	6109	1941	⅞ Cu.Yds.	18ft 6ins	(c)	(8)

(a)   New 6/1937 (per R&R); erected on site 1937–9
(b)   New 6/1937 (per R&R); arrived 11/1938, erected on site by 1939
(c)   ?

(1)   Ebbw Vale Qy 1938; at Irthlingborough 1943; to Buccleuch Qy c 1944. s/s
(2)   Calcine Bank. To Irthlingborough 12/1938. s/s
(3)   Buccleuch Qy. To Blisworth Quarries c 1954
(4)   Buccleuch Qy. Scr c 7/1948
(5)   New to Harrowden Lane Clamps. Buccleuch Qy by 1946. To Blisworth Quarries 1954
(6)   s/s
(7)   New to Harrowden Lane Clamps. Buccleuch Qy 1944/5. To Scunthorpe 2/1949
(8)   New to Harrowden Lane. To Buccleuch Qy c 1944. To South Wales, per MOS, 9/1945

THE IRTHLINGBOROUGH GROUP

There were three quarries at Ditchford and two at Irthlingborough, all small and with a paucity of information about them matched by the physical remains. Only the vast mining complex at Irthlingborough commands attention, from almost any aspect. It was a product of wartime, by the South Wales ironmasters, Ebbw Vale Steel, Iron & Coal Co Ltd, who feared for the loss of ore supplies from Spain; production at Irthlingborough did not however commence until after the end of hostilities and fell far short of that anticipated. Ebbw Vale itself came to grief in the Depression, and their assets were taken over by Richard Thomas & Co Ltd, who proceeded to develop the mines on a grand scale (again as a wartime measure) but with considerable modification to the processing plant. The internal tramway systems were unique, with dozens of electric locomotives, a few diesels, and an interesting collection of steam on the standard gauge connection to the LMSR. And it has been very well documented. So let us move on.

DITCHFORD (IRTHLINGBOROUGH) QUARRY

Owner T.W. Ward

This quarry was essentially a wartime unit as far as production is concerned, but negotiations began in 1912; Irthlingborough UDC were considering an application for a level crossing of Ditchford Lane in May 1912[1] and the siding agreement with the LNWR is dated 6th June 1912. Production commenced in 1913, according to LQ; the latter source quotes the quarry as disused in 1918, and the LNWR siding was taken out on 27th October 1918. Whilst the full extent of working is not known, it was evidently only on a small scale. The LNWR station diagram shows a short siding east of the level crossing, with a narrow gauge tramway alongside indicating that side-tipping was utilized. The tramway crossed Ditchford Road on the level, climbing obliquely to the quarry on the west

Ditchford Quarries (T.W. Ward). The approach to the former Ditchford station, 2nd February 1969. Wards quarries lay to the left of the lane, with the tramway crossing the road by the roofless building – believed to have been the weighhouse – to enter the station yard at the right. Ian L. Wright

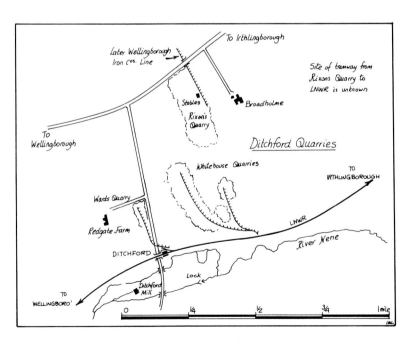

161

side of the road at the top of the bank. Horses were probably used for hauling over the short distance involved; it is not impossible, but unlikely, that a locomotive was used. A ruined building west of the road, believed to have been a weighhouse, stood in the 1950's, but has now disappeared, along with virtually all other traces of this little-known system. The site of the LNWR siding has been erased (1978) by the Anglian Water Authority in converting the trackbed of the railway into a roadway to a new sewage treatment plant. The tramway road crossing is indicated by a fence on the east side and (obliquely opposite) a gap in the hedge where hawthorn gives way to elder, on the west. The field beyond is sunken below road level but the main quarry area further up has been filled in; an ancient signpost inscribed 'Tip closed. By order' lolling drunkenly in the hedge reveals that reclamation of quarry sites by 'infilling' is nothing new! Outcropping stone exists in the fields higher up the hill.

Footnote

1.   *Evening Telegraph*, 23rd May 1912. Thanks to Richard Sherwood for this item.

Grid References

930685	Tipping dock to LNWR
930685	Level crossing

DITCHFORD QUARRIES

Owners: Rixon & Co; Rixon's Iron & Brick Co Ltd from 18th June 1883

These quarries are not specifically mentioned in MS, doubtless because the output was lumped with that from the company's pits at Finedon; we only came to hear of them from Mr Field, in the 1950's a foreman at Wellingborough quarries, who pointed out the stables used by Rixon's horses for hauling the tubs of ironstone. These stables lay about 200 yards south of the Wellingborough-Irthlingborough road opposite West Field Lodge and the pits may be presumed to have been close by. From these a tramway ran down to the LNWR east of Ditchford station; the line is not shown on the 1884 OS and the LNWR Working Timetable of November 1886 gives the quarries as closed (Thanks to Mr A.St G. Walsh for this information). The same source lists the siding as 'W & Rixon', suggesting possibly a common tipping dock with the Whitehouse quarries described below. That is all we know; quarrying probably started in the late 1870's, following Finedon, and the tramway may have been of the same 3ft 3ins gauge. The quarries were later reopened by Wellingborough Iron Co Ltd (which see for further information). The stables – a wooden shed with a long slatted louvre – was leased to a farmer and was in excellent condition, but was demolished about 1982. Of the tramway route and connection to the LNWR no traces are visible.

DITCHFORD QUARRIES

Owners; Thomas Whitehouse: Thrapston Iron Ore Co Ltd from 1875; Butlin Bevan & Co Ltd from 1879.

A lease of three fields, totalling 47 acres in extent and forming an area bounded by the LNWR Northampton–Peterborough line on the south, and Ditchford Road on the west, were leased by the Ecclesiastical Commissioners, with the agreement of the vicar and the patron of the living, George Wentworth Fitzwilliam, to Thomas Whitehouse, coal merchant, of Northampton; the term was for 14 years from 1st April

1873. The 6 ins OS of 1884 shows a tramway of narrow gauge (presumed from its end-on connection at a siding on the LNWR line) along the eastern extremity of the property, with a worked-out section to the west; as the quarries were closed in 1885, the alignment was probably the final one, working having commenced at the western side. No details of equipment are known, nor are there any recognisable traces of what must have been an outcrop site. The site of the tip to the LNWR can however be identified, even though there are no physical traces surviving; the leased ground abuts on the railway mostly well above rail level to give a one-sided 'cutting' (the other side being level with the river meadows) – but at one point this is only a matter of feet, and this is where the tip was placed. The railbed has now been adapted for use by the Anglian Water Authority for access to a new sewage treatment plant, with little alteration to the topography.

Grid Reference

936685   Tipping dock to LNWR

Ditchford Quarries (Rixon).   Stables for horses used by Rixon in the 1880s. This building, photographed 30th January 1980, lasted until about 1982. The later Wellingborough Iron Co tramway (locomotive worked) ran to the left of the stables.   Eric Tonks

IRTHLINGBOROUGH MINES AND QUARRIES

Owners: Ebbw Vale Steel, Iron & Coal Co Ltd; Richard Thomas & Co Ltd from 3rd April 1936; Richard Thomas & Baldwins Ltd from 3rd January 1945.

At the end of World War I there were two sets of workings at Finedon, nibbling away at the outcrop stone around the 250-foot contour east of the Ise; these were Barlow's Finedon pits and Keeble & Jellett's Finedon Park pits, with tramways down to the Midland Railway main line. The corresponding outcrop south of Irthlingborough had also been worked by two companies – Irthlingborough Iron Ore Co Ltd and Arthur Dunmore – but only in a desultory sort of way. The ironstone bed continued under heavier cover in a broad band from the west of Irthlingborough northwards to Cranford, and mining had already been undertaken at the south and north ends (Thingdon and Cranford mines respectively). The extensive block between, stretching from north of Irthlingborough and east of Finedon to Burton Wold, was untouched, and it was this area that the Ebbw Vale Steel, Iron & Coal Co Ltd chose to develop on a large scale; a survey on their behalf appears to have been made in 1909 but no positive moves were made until after the outbreak of World War I, when it became imperative to have adequate supplies of home ore rather than foreign.

The Plevins-Kidner 'Poplar Lodge' lease of 1893 (see under 'Finedon Quarries' for further details) was due to expire on 25th March 1914, and this property of 210 acres passed to EVSIC and was augmented by neighbouring properties to the south, totalling 366 acres. Finedon Park pits were then in operation by R.E. Campbell (who had taken over from Keeble & Jellett) and the Finedon Park estate of 250 acres was purchased from him 9th November 1915, along with his other property at Denford, near Ringstead, on the recommendation of Dr Henry Louis, minerals advisor to EVSIC. These major purchases were followed over the next two years by the acquisition of more than twenty mostly small areas, to give the company mining and quarrying rights over about 1800 acres. With the exception of Finedon Park on the fringe of their area, where opencast working would continue (see the appropriate section) the aim from the start was to mine, with a cover of some 80 feet.

Mr A.J. Pack, former surveyor with Richard Thomas & Baldwins Ltd, retained in his personal files a great deal of very interesting archival material, that he kindly allowed us to inspect. From the files of correspondence between Fred (later Sir Frederick) Mills (managing director of EVSIC) and Dr Henry Louis (minerals advisor) and Messrs Foster and Cranfield (mineral agents), emerge some interesting details on transport proposals. The initial scheme was to use the existing outlet to the Midland Railway from Finedon Park, continuing the 2ft 6ins tramway from the latter, across the Wellingborough road to Neville's Lodge, a distance of about one mile. This was to be a double track line operated by petrol locomotives, the first known suggestion of such traction in the ironstone fields. The shortcomings of the scheme were soon apparent; the route would cross the Wellingborough Iron Co's metre line, which in itself would not cause much difficulty, and the latter company's mining area, which would, because of disturbance to the trackbed. The alternative of an overhead ropeway over the same route was hardly any better, as pylons could be affected by mining; so the idea was put forward of a ropeway from Neville's Lodge in the opposite direction, via White Lodge to the LNWR line, a different approach that provided the key to the scheme adopted – to drive a tunnel at a convenient point to open up the whole of the central block. Endless rope haulage was suggested first but electric locomotives were decided upon instead. The disued Metropolitan Brickworks lay on the proposed route and it was suggested that this works be bought and the kilns used for experiments in calcining.

There is plenty of evidence of care in the planning of the mining system. Commencing in January 1916, a tunnel was driven in a nearly northwesterly direction in the hillside southeast of Irthlingborough, on the lower slopes of which a series of calcining kilns were erected; after calcination, the ore was to be loaded into railway wagons on a siding connecting with the LNWR Northampton–Peterborough line, which gave better access to Ebbw Vale than the Midland Railway. There were already two sidings off the LNWR – to British Portland Cement Manufacturers Ltd (originally laid for Arthur Dunmore) and to Hatton Shaw (Irthlingborough) Ltd (originally laid for Irthlingborough Iron Ore Co Ltd) – and EVSIC made an agreement with the LNWR to use the latter, extending it to serve their battery of kilns. They also purchased 106 acres of adjoining land from John Spencer, at the same time agreeing to allow Hatton Shaw the use of the siding for their railborne traffic. An arrangement was also made with BPCM to use their connection for a couple of years, presumably for constructional purposes, and to divert

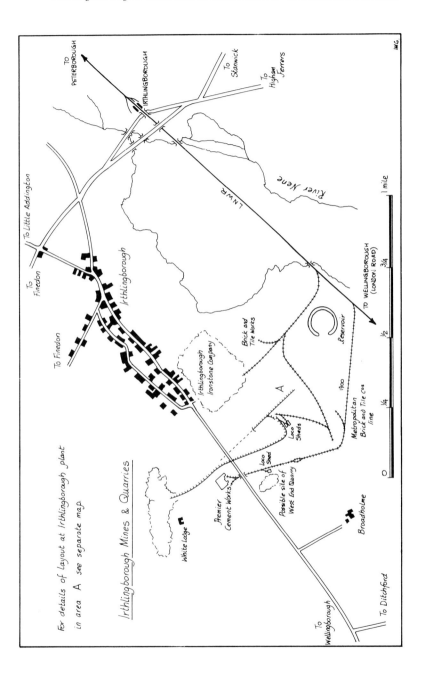

their line to the west in one part, doubtless to clear their sidings; though it does not seem that this was done.

Before describing the plant, mention must be made of one exploratory development, interesting mainly for its tramway. Ebbw Vale leased from BPCM a 93.6 acre site northwest of White Lodge for 21 years from 25th March 1916; this was primarily for the purpose of driving their tunnel under the site, but on the top it was proposed to open trial pits and to take away the output a 3ft gauge tramway was laid between the pits and the headquarters site down the hill. This line crossed the Wellingborough road on the level near Pine Lodge, and permission was obtained from Irthlingborough UDC to convey 'ironstone etc in tubs drawn by a locomotive' for one year from 1st July 1916, renewable annually. The locomotive was a secondhand Hudswell Clarke. A building down by the standard gauge locomotive shed is believed to have housed her. The last record of the authority to cross the road is dated 30th June 1925, according to Irthlingborough UDC records (thanks are due to Russell Wear for this information). This line, though short-lived, has left traces of its course north of the road – in fact they show up better than most of the standard gauge system!

The mines were worked on the usual 'pillar and stall' system, with a 3ft gauge tramway to take away the ore. The main adit, which was used also for haulage, was bricked throughout, and ran north with a bearing of 316° from the entrance, on a rising gradient of 1/200 to assist drainage, for about 1000 yards when working began. Headings into the orebed, and cross galleries parallel to the main haulage way, divided the ironstone into 'pillars', which allowed extraction of 85% of the ore. The height of the galleries was about eight feet, a reasonable headroom, and working conditions were good, with ample ventilation, freedom from dust, and a temperature of 50–5°F throughout the year. A rather unusual provision was a brick staircase to the surface to save miners nearly a mile detour; 'Steps Entrance' was not far from Neville's Lodge.

With the adit some 75 feet above the level of the LNWR, advantage could be taken of gravity in operating the plant, which was built by Hanson & Son Ltd of Wellingborough and was a pioneer of its kind in being constructed throughout of reinforced concrete to save steel; a very detailed account has been published.[1] Emerging from the adit, the double tramway ran first in cutting, on an embankment and then over a concrete bridge at a rising gradient to a service bunker at the centre of a row of 16 Gyers kilns, 30 feet high, running transversely to the tramway. The trams

Irthlingborough Mines and Quarries (Ebbw Vale/Richard Thomas)

Irthlingborough Mines. Construction of the adit and approach tramway. Collection A.J. Pack

Irthlingborough Mines. Aerial view of the original Ebbw Vale plant, with the row of kilns and service gantry in the foreground. Main tunnel entrance at centre left, with narrow gauge tramway route to the gantry elevated at the lower end and then carried on a concrete bridge to the gantry. Note the predominating use of concrete, to save steel (this being wartime). Standard gauge wagons on line by kilns. Workshops and other buildings to left and right of main route. Irthlingborough village upper right, with Wellingborough road running across to left. Smoke drifts from the cement works chimney at upper left.   RTB

Irthlingborough Mines.   The original Ebbw Vale plant of 16 Gyers kilns for calcining the
ironstone. c.1920.   B.W. Jakes/Collection Greg Evans

were hauled up the bridge by a 'creeper' engaging the tram axles, to a
tippler from which the loads were discharged into the bunker, and from
the latter into one of a pair of charging cars running along the tops of the
kilns. Each car received the requisite amount of fuel from a bucket
elevator for admixture before being emptied into the kiln. The outgoing
tram automatically operated the tippler mechanism for the next full
tram, and then ran to a retarding creeper on the incline bridge for return
to the mine. The ore was loaded by hand into the wagons, which had steel
sides on a steel frame, and held a nominal three tons, but it was found
that skilled loaders could fill them with 3½ tons, with care in building up
the sides. Traction on the tramway was provided by electric locomotives;
in the underground working galleries small battery-driven locomotives
(British Electric Vehicles No. 1 type) were used to haul wagons into a loop
for collection by the larger overhead-wire locomotives. The small battery
locomotives weighed two tons, had three speeds and worked at 50 volts,
and they remained underground continuously except for repairs; they
had a battery capacity of 52 ampere-hours and did eight hours duty
alternating with eight hours on charge. The horsepower had been quoted
as 4.8 but a 1939 inventory by Richard Thomas & Co Ltd gives only Nos.
10 and 11 as 4.8, the rest as 2 horsepower, which seems a more likely

figure. There were fourteen of these machines, numbered 1–14, supplied between March 1919 and February 1922, and two similar in design were built in Irthlingborough shops, numbered 15 and 16. However, the last two are not listed in the 1939 inventory, the explanation for which is not apparent – and we had better not guess. It seems probable that some exchange of numbers took place later on, as one of the home-built machines was said to be No. 7. Repair of locomotives and other plant was carried out in two large buildings, housing extensive workshops and laboratories, between adit and kilns.

For haulage to the kilns, two locomotives were supplied by the General Electric Co of Schenectady, USA, in 1916; they were seven-ton machines with two 25 horsepower motors working at 250 volts, and they collected current from overhead wires by a trolley. Generally the trolleys were trailed, but sometimes underground the trolleys were pushed to the first crossing, and care had to be exercised. These locomotives feature in a commemorative booklet published by British Thomson-Houston Co Ltd,[2] but the 1939 inventory leaves no doubt they they were built in America, a view supported by a recollection (handed down like a piece of folklore) of their arriving at Irthlingborough suffering from seawater damage through enemy action en route. What part was played by BTH is uncertain – perhaps the order was placed with them but transferred to their American associates because of wartime difficulties, or possibly the damaged locomotives were sent to BTH for refurbishment.

When the 'Eb. Vale' – as it was locally known – arrived, it was at first welcomed as an employer, especially after the war, when jobs were becoming increasingly hard to get; in addition to the mines, the company hoped to establish an iron and steel works. This did not come to pass, probably because of the worsening postwar conditions, but mining was developed on the lines envisaged.

The potential mining area was increased by further purchases, the most important being from William Robb – 113 acres on 12th September 1917 (areas worked previously by the Glendon Iron Co) and, on 10th September 1917, 887 acres including Buccleuch and Glebe farms and the Burton Wold area, making a total of some 3000 acres. There were also a few sales of land, e.g. 26 acres to Irthlingborough UDC in 1921 for the 'Garden Village' scheme, this on land that had been worked out by Irthlingborough Iron Ore Co Ltd. A small area of 7¼ acres was leased to Charles Barlow on 1st December 1919, next to his 'Cricket Field' pit, for nine years, and mostly returned to EVSIC 3rd October 1925.

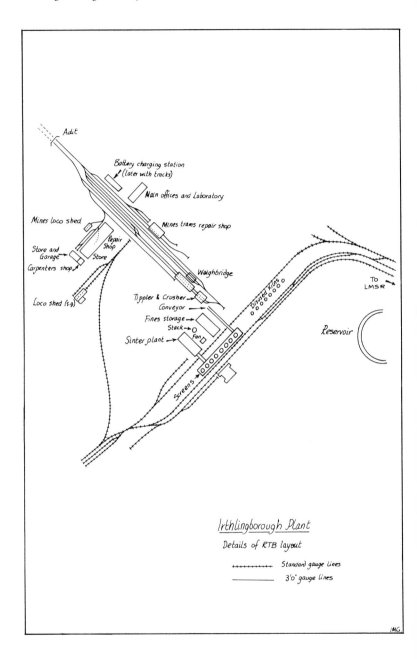

Adit

Battery charging station
(later with tracks)

Main offices and Laboratory

Mines loco shed

Mines trams repair shop

Repair
Shop

Store and
Garage
Store

Carpenters shop

Loco shed (s.g.)

Weighbridge

Tippler & Crusher
Conveyor
Fines storage
Stack
Sinter plant
Fan

Screens

Disused Kilns

To
LMSR

Reservoir

Irthlingborough Plant

Details of RTB layout

┼┼┼┼┼┼┼┼┼ Standard gauge lines

────────── 3'0" gauge lines

JMG.

The plant was completed in 1919 and production began; the exact date is not certain, but there was an official opening of the new mine in August 1920, when a special train carried guests from Euston, running into the company's sidings.[3] The original aim of sending out 2000 tons of ore every 24 hours was not realised because of the reduced postwar demand, and in fact there were a number of temporary closures, the longest being from early 1923 to February 1925 (*'Kettering Leader'*, 6th February 1925). During this period the premises of Hatton Shaw were also closed and the auction sale of plant here was advertised in the 'Evening Telegraph' of 24th February 1923. At the time of maximum output about 400 men were employed but in 1925 there were but 85.[4] Throughout the Depression production continued at a low level (about 2000 tons per week), with the parent company in financial difficulties that resulted in the acquisition of the Ebbw Vale works by Richard Thomas & Co Ltd in December 1935. The Irthlingborough properties came into the Richard Thomas fold on 3rd April 1936 and in due time entered a more active phase involving a very thorough reorganisation of the plant. Not only that; in addition to the mines, Richard Thomas opened a large quarry – Buccleuch – on the outskirts of Finedon. The latter was really an extension under heavier cover of Barlow's Finedon quarries, and is dealt with under that section; but from the outset it was regarded as part of the Irthlingborough system and came under the same manager, W.E. Davies, whose weekly reports (preserved in BSC archives) give a detailed account of events in both environments. The aim was to increase production, as Irthlingborough/Finedon was to supply Redbourn Works at Scunthorpe in addition to Ebbw Vale; even so, mines output never exceeded 7000 tons per week – less than Ebbw Vale's original target – largely due to chronic labour troubles that plagued Irthlingborough throughout its history. The manager commented at the start that the local miners came from an agricultural background with no previous mining experience, but later the main competition came from the local boot and shoe industry.

Buccleuch quarry was part of the ground purchased in 1919 by Ebbw Vale from William Robb, but never developed by them either by quarrying or mining. Another opencast site can also be dealt with here, as it fits chronologically. One of the smaller parcels of land at Irthlingborough was acquired from Glover's Trust, and with it were a couple of fields (of 53 acres) at Stone Cross, by the junction of the Wellingborough and Ditchford roads. It was proposed to open up this area, and to make it more worthwhile an adjoining area was purchased in 1937 from Locket Chapman. It was of course quite isolated from Irthlingborough or Finedon, and the output was to be conveyed by aerial ropeway to the Buccleuch Quarry despatch point. R. White & Sons of Widnes quoted for a ropeway of 1425 yards, with electrical haulage, and hods holding 3½ tons of ore. This plan was not implemented and part of the site was subsequently leased to Wellingborough Iron Co Ltd, but they too ignored it.

The existing mining system was extended north and east, southeast of Finedon beyond the Irthlingborough by-pass road, and a branch of the main underground line was driven to emerge near the eastern end of the old Cricket Field quarry that Barlow's once worked, at the southern end of the new Buccleuch quarry then being developed, so that the quarry output could be conveyed through the tunnel to the pre-processing plant. The line from the Finedon adit ran east-north-east to join the main tramway a little northeast of Bank Farm, but with a cutoff also to the south of the farm; this is believed to have been done to provide airways. Francois Cementation Co Ltd carried out most of the work, bringing up the total tunnel length to 4450 yards. The calcining kilns were no longer

Irthlingborough Mines. The main tunnel, with a Ruston & Hornsby locomotive hauling a loaded train, 12th April 1938. Locomotive is 44/48hp class, either 187074 or 187076. RH

Irthlingborough Mines. Aerial photograph of the plant, April 1960. Note circular reservoir lower centre, with tramway connection to RTB just to the right, and the route of the connection to the cement works to the left; BR route between them. The row of kilns can be seen, and the main tunnel entrance. Main road to Wellingborough runs diagonally across the centre from Irthlingborough village, right; the 'Model Village' south of this. Cement works area immediately north of the road, with quarries visible. The two light swathes are Wellingborough No. 5 (lower) and Wellingborough No. 6 (upper) quarries. Dark area to right of the latter is formed by the trees on Finedon No. 1 quarry. RTB

used as such; the northern eight were disused, the other eight converted to storage hoppers for ore, crushed coke and sintered ore. Crushing and sintering plants were installed and also a new wagon tippler; ore from the tipplers (each of which held two wagons) was conveyed by belt ('the Lambeth Walk') to the crusher and then passed through a two-stage screening plant, the oversize going to Redbourn Works, the smaller material being mixed with coke breeze and sintered for Ebbw Vale. Crushed or sintered ore was stored in the bunkers (ex-kilns) and discharged into hopper wagons from the bases. When loaded, the wagons ran down to an exchange point by gravity, to be picked up by the main line locomotive; the Irthlingborough engine merely took them up from the junction and marshalled them in the sidings ready for running to the plant. Track was chaired mainly, with a few sections of modern flat-bottomed rail; sleepers were wood, with a few concrete. The locomotive shed was isolated from the rest of the standard gauge system and only reached by a very stiff bank from the level of the plant; possibly this was so that locomotives requiring repairs would be easily accessible to machine shop personnel. The main line junction was protected by a signal box ('Irthlingborough Iron Co's Siding') and a gate over the access siding.

To deal with the increased output, the narrow gauge locomotive stock was augmented by the purchase of six three-ton 4½ horsepower battery locomotives by Greenwood & Batley, larger than the BEV machines, for service in the galleries, and four overhead wire locomotives, also by Greenwood & Batley, of 7½ tons and with two 40 hp motors. Two Ruston & Hornsby 48 hp diesel locomotives were also obtained, one being kept at the end of the line serving Buccleuch quarry, marshalling wagons ready for the electric locomotive to pick up; the other was kept at Irthlingborough as spare, but also used to help out at the southern end of the tunnel as required. The layout at Irthlingborough was basically similar to that obtaining in Ebbw Vale days, but modified to suit the new procedure; the concrete bridge to the gantry over the kilns was no longer used, the new tippler lying about a hundred yards north of the old one, and linked to the crusher, as noted above.

On the main haulage road T-section rail, 50 lbs per yard was laid on wooden sleepers 4ft 9ins by 6ins by 4ins; on the mine branch roads was 35 lb rail in 12ft lengths dogged to wooden sleepers 4ft by 6ins by 3ins. Point sets were in 12-foot lengths welded to flat steel sleepers, so that they could replace any 12-foot section of track.

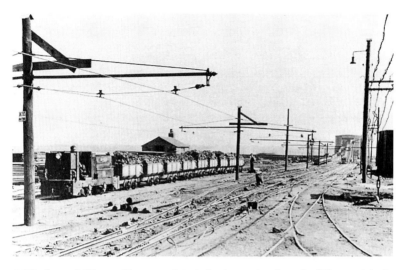

Irthlingborough Mines.   The approach to the bunker serving the rank of kilns as originally built by Ebbw Vale. A Ruston & Hornsby locomotive stands at the head of a loaded train. Note overhead cables for the trolley locomotives. 12th April 1938.   Ruston & Hornsby

Irthlingborough Mines.   Ebbw Vale built a rake of 16 kilns for calcining the ore. When RT took over the plant, the southern 8 were converted to storage hoppers; the northern 8 were disused, and, as the photo shows, the end pair were dismantled. 1st September 1965.

Ian L. Wright

Irthlingborough Mines.   A topside view of the disused kilns, with a train approaching the works from the BR line in the background.   RTB

Production commenced 28th September 1938 from the mine, and quickly increased to 6000 tons per week by June 1940: initially the ratio of mine to quarry ore was kept at 1 to 3, but improved sintering capacity enabled a 1 to 1 ratio to be reached. A further 'main line' battery locomotive arrived in May 1941. This was the busiest period for the Irthlingborough system, as demanded by wartime conditions; but the company was continually beset by labour difficulties – much absenteeism and the departure of miners to more congenial work in the local shoe factories. To alleviate the position some Italian prisoners-of-war were allocated in September 1942, while after the war (in July 1947) came a contingent of Polish workers from Podington Camp; the latter proved a more permanent transfer, and the present BSC East Midland Regional Records Centre at Irthlingborough was formerly used as a hostel for Polish workers, later revamped for the use of Italian workers and called an 'Hotel', opened by the Italian Ambassador.

Mechanical improvements were also introduced in the form of 'Eimco' Rock Shovels, the first three arriving in December 1945; two more came in February 1947, and probably two more after that. The face layout was modified to suit these loaders, with two tracks; on one road the loader was filling a tub, with empties on the other road, and a locomotive in attendance. A team of six men were employed at each position – two drillers, one shotfirer, the shovel operator, a wagon-loader (a youth) and a track-layer; the output of each team averaged 850 tons per day. Loaded by hand, the tubs could be made to hold 3½ tons, by placing larger lumps round the edges, but with mechanical loading, once the 2½ tons load had been put in, the rest started to overflow, thus negating the advantages of quick loading. Finishing off by hand was too slow, so 9 inch steel extensions were welded to the original wagon bodies to allow them to hold 3½ tons. This was introduced in January 1946. Six more Greenwood & Batley mine locomotives came in July 1947, and six more in June 1950. The pattern of pillars in the mine changed too, and is well shown in the plan of workings; in Ebbw Vale days and before the advent of mechanical loaders, the cross headings were fairly close together, but in the postwar years were much fewer, which led to some difficulties of irregular collapsing when the mines were abandoned.

The standard gauge line was worked by steam locomotives throughout, and a mixed lot they were, all secondhand. The first was an ancient 4-4-OT designed for passenger traffic, a throw-out of Ebbw Vale and quite unsuited to the grade at Irthlingborough; she was soon replaced by a

Irthlingborough Mines.   Rotary tipplers for emptying mines tubs into the crusher.   RTB

Irthlingborough Mines.   Mines battery locomotive of the GB 1569–74 series. Note overhead cable for trolley locomotive.   RTB

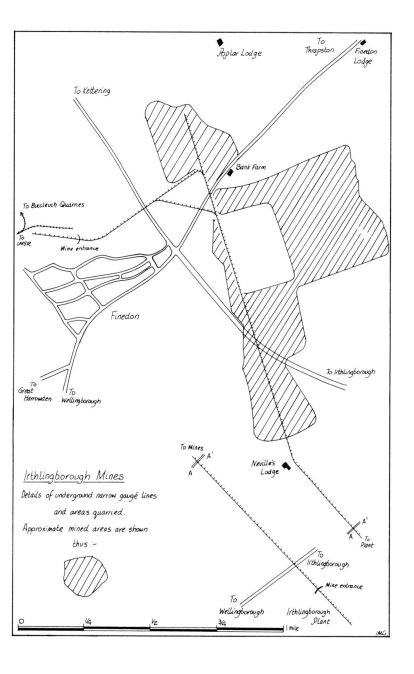

Irthlingborough Mines. General view of yard, looking towards the tipplers, and showing the way in which the haulage cables were accommodated at crossovers. 18th September 1964.   G.H. Starmer

Irthlingborough Mines. Researchers into ironstone history will recognise this building, which has had an interesting history. Originally a County Council workhouse, then a remand home, it was taken over by Richard Thomas & Co Ltd as a hostel for Polish workers, then by Italians. The view was taken at the official opening by the Italian Ambassador. It later became the East Midlands Regional Records Centre for the British Steel Corporation.   RTB

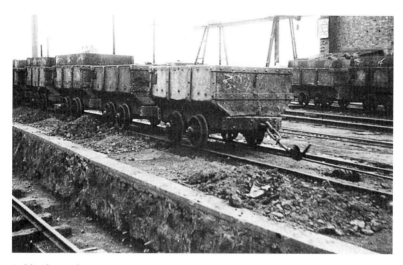

Irthlingborough Mines. Locomotives were used to haul the trains out of the mines into the main yard, where a shackle was attached to the leading wagon and the train then hauled by cable to the tipplers. Note wagons with and without extensions. 27th May 1965.

S.A. Leleux

Irthlingborough Mines. A standard 3ft gauge tube with the sides extended to increase capacity. In hand-loading days, careful stacking enabled a load of 3½ tons to be carried, but with mechanical loading it became necessary to provide extra support to achieve the same loading. 27th May 1965. S.A. Leleux

four-coupled saddle tank with the strange name SUNSHINE. A photograph taken in 1936 when the engine was lying out of use suggests it as a product of one of the firms who 'built' locomotives from a number of secondhand machines, not necessarily by the same maker; in the present case, Black Hawthorn elements predominate. To help her, a machine much better suited to the working conditions arrived in due course: a six-coupled Peckett that had a few years previously worked at the Finedon Park quarries; she still carried No. 9 (of her original owners) on brass plates on the saddle tank but had also acquired a small oval plate with the plain 28 of the Ebbw Vale list on the cabside. The next engine was another six-wheeler, this time with inside cylinders, a Robert Stephenson product named STEPHENSON; this came from Ebbw Vale also, but had originally been Port Talbot Railway No. 1. These last two locomotives were painted black with red coupling rods, later green, lined yellow and with red rods. STEPHENSON was withdrawn in 1958 and slowly dismantled over a long period, from January 1959 to April 1960.

HENRY CORT was perhaps the best-known of the Irthlingborough fleet, if only because she later went to preservation; she arrived from Blisworth without any nameplates (one of which at least had been lying in the shed at Blisworth for some time) but at Irthlingborough plates appeared – on the cabside this time instead of the saddle tank – in 1960. She had a livery of dark green with yellow and black dazzle stripes on the buffer beam. AB 1466, known as FRANCE, as this had been its name one time, was dark green with a single white line; this latter locomotive was for some reason not very popular at Irthlingborough. The last arrival was another Peckett design, but had been built at Ebbw Vale in 1909 from parts supplied by Pecketts; she was green, with red-backed nameplates, and being eleven tons heavier than HENRY CORT, was the preferred locomotive, at least under wintry conditions. Rumours of the possible purchase of a 200hp Sentinel were around in 1964 but nothing materialised.

We must now return to the narrow gauge, where big changes were introduced in the early 1960's as a result of a decision by the Inspector of Mines to impose full mining regulations; amongst other things, it would be required to have every 50 yards of the overhead wiring system independently connected and therefore isolatable. This would have been an extremely costly exercise, and instead it was decided to abandon the overhead wire system completely and to convert the locomotives concerned to battery power. *'Electrical Times'* of 19th June 1963 contains an account of the new equipment and how it met the basic requirement

Irthlingborough Mines. The mystery standard gauge locomotive, known as 'SUNSHINE', out of use on 3rd August 1936. The origin and identity of this engine are unknown, and she appears to incorporate parts from different builders. G. Alliez/Courtesy B.D. Stoyel

Irthlingborough Mines. A poor photograph but an interesting subject. No. 9 (P 751) saw service at the Finedon Park quarries, then went to Ebbw Vale steelworks, returning to Northamptonshire about 1925. Collection Greg Evans

Irthlingborough Mines.   The most interesting of the standard gauge locomotive stock was this 0-6-0ST STEPHENSON (RS 2837) which at one time was Port Talbot Railway No. 1 and which later came into the ownership of Ebbw Vale Steel Iron & Coal Co Ltd. 18th July 1958.
R.M. Casserley

Irthlingborough Mines.   AB 1466 outside the locomotive shed, 21st May 1964. Though carrying no name, she was called 'FRANCE', the name carried in the past.   S.A. Leleux

for a locomotive capable of doing seven round trips (a total of 56 miles) without recharging. The battery capacity was split – a smaller unit on the locomotive itself, and a much larger set of batteries on a trailer; the loco. was restricted to shunting and running round the trailer at termini, and with the trailer unit was used for train haulage, with a safety device to negate any attempt to start the train with the loco. power only. D.P. Battery Co Ltd of Bakewell supplied the equipment, and the first conversion (of No. 5) was completed in March 1962, and painted grey with black and white dazzle sides. Following the success of this unit, Nos. 3, 4 and 6 were similarly converted in 1964, but the old American locomotives were not so treated. A spacious new charging shed was built in 1962. In this period a start was made in renumbering the Greenwood & Batley battery locomotives with fluorescent numbers; hitherto they carried the last two digits of the makers' numbers, e.g. GB 1569 was number 69 – as it happened, there were no duplications, the numbers being 61–3/9–74/8–80/91–6. They were now designed to become 17 upwards, following on the BEV machines. In the event, only eight were so treated, in the order they came through shops.

While the conversion to battery power was under review and test, a fleet of Ruston & Hornsby mines diesel locomotives were obtained from Dorman Long's ironstone mines in the Cleveland area, the first six arriving in 1962 to help out in the mine until such time as battery locomotives could take over. In addition there were the two Rustons that had worked at the Finedon end of the tunnel, and which had been transferred to Irthlingborough about 1945. Further Rustons arrived from Dorman Long in 1964, several of 2ft 6ins gauge, and were cheaply acquired purely as a source of spares; they were all stored in the battery-charging shed, a motley lot of semi-dismantled machines. When they arrived, these diesels were all in green livery with yellow and black dazzle ends, but 418803 was repainted orange – the only one so treated. The pair from Finedon were grey with black and white dazzle ends. RH 433388 was grey with black and white lining.

The main narrow gauge rolling stock consisted of some 560 steel wagons carrying steel numbers welded on the side. In addition there were two pairs of vehicles for carrying men in and out of the mine; they were of steel, with a roof of steel, and window spaces. At one time there may have been a four-wheeled petrol locomotive for yard shunting, but this has not been confirmed. There were two steel-bodied, wooden-framed side-tippers, said to have been used in the construction period; a water

Irthlingborough Mines. The imposition of much stricter regulations concerning the use of trolley locomotives underground led RTB to convert the GB examples in 1962–4 to battery operation, including a heavy truck to carry the extra batteries. The photograph shows one of the locomotives pushing a train towards the mines.   RTB

tank wagon; and two flat wagons. The last acquisitions were eight flat wagons built by the Cambrian Wagon Works, Cardiff, and received in April 1965; they had bodies 8ft 1ins x 4ft 6ins x 1½ins, on a wheelbase of 3ft 9ins, and were used for carrying points and other equipment.

During all this time the tunnel outlet at the Finedon end was still open, though covered by a stout wire grille, and in 1964 a new ventilation shaft close by was opened, similarly protected from unauthorised entry. However, all these far-reaching plans and replacement of plant were all too soon overtaken by closure. The shutdown at Irthlingborough was rather more sudden than at opencast quarries that were closed around the same period, and full production (then running at some 4500 tons per week) was maintained to the last day, 30th September 1965. In fact, the closure had been announced in the first week of July, yet the Northampton Chronicle & Echo of 19th July 1965 contained a reference to the extension of ironstone mining in the parishes of Burton Latimer, Finedon, Irthlingborough and Little Addington, permission for which had been given by the Ministry of Housing and Local Government, subject to the customary safeguards against subsidence and restoration to agricultural use. There was a (very) belated formal consent to mining under the Town & Country Planning Act of 1947; mining had been carried on under an 'Interim Development Order' that in fact covered the entire period of operation. The reason for the closure was stated to be the cost of transport, to South Wales in particular.

Officially the works was put on a 'care and maintenance' basis that would permit quick reopening if desired; but in fact dismantlement of the equipment in the mine started almost immediately, and beneath roads the tunnels were being filled up solid, rendering any reopening very unlikely. Nevertheless, pulling out of the mine was a lengthy business that was not completed until the very end of 1966; the narrow gauge was used for bringing rail out, RH 418803 being one of the regular 'demolition train' locomotives, and about one hundred yards of tunnel were cleared each week. In the autumn of 1966 all the wagons were out of the mine and were cut up at the rate of 60–70 per week – it is believed, by W.J. Redden of Wellingborough. When everything was out of the mine, the entrance was bricked up and the familiar 'safety first' notice painted on the lintel had gone. Some of the narrow gauge locomotives were cut up in 1966 but the bulk of them remained throughout the winter, the last being taken away 4th March 1967 by T.W. Sheppard of Wellingborough,

Irthlingborough Mines. While the trolley locomotives were being converted to battery power, a fleet of discarded RH locomotives was purchased from Dorman Long's Cleveland mines. Few of them ever turned a wheel in service, but provided spares for those that did. Some were 3ft gauge, others 2ft 6ins. Our photograph shows nine of them in the battery charging shed – on 21st May 1964. S.A. Leleux

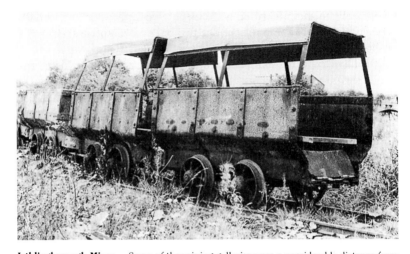

Irthlingborough Mines. Some of the mining galleries were a considerable distance from the entrance, and a few wagons were converted into crude 'carriages' for the miners. Those shown were photographed on 18th September 1965 near the battery-charging shed.

G.H. Starmer

acting as agents for Thos. W. Ward Ltd.

Dismantling of the surface plant commenced in the spring of 1966, and by the autumn most of the kilns had been demolished. Lifting of the standard gauge line took place in the summer and was done in conjunction with the company's line from the Finedon quarries to BR, that had been abandoned for twenty years. The substantial buildings were left – the steel and concrete engineering shops, the brick locomotive shed and smithy, and the offices – and there were odd lengths of track embedded in concrete. The embankment that formerly carried eight parallel narrow gauge tracks was extant, but the end where the tipplers stood had been removed, leaving a sheer drop, with nothing at the lower level. In June 1968 Mr Sweeting, the last works manager, though now retired, was still paying calls at the site of his former employment, doubtless thinking of times past.

The rail tracks were lifted, the kilns demolished, and the buildings stripped of machinery, afterwards being left as they were, a prey to the elements and to vandals, both of which took their toll over the years. The two tall machine shops, gutted, windowless and beginning to lose roof tiles, were still impressive in 1979, and here and there in the concrete floors were lengths of embedded narrow gauge track. The course of the main tracks to the bricked-up adit was still very clear and the wooden sheds alongside were in position. The two steam locomotive sheds – the old narrow gauge shed and the more modern standard gauge one – survived, and from the latter the course of the line was traceable all the way to the BR trackbed; the section at river level will probably disappear soon under the extensive gravel workings, the lorries serving which use the BR trackbed for egress.

Some of the ground near the Wellingborough road was in 1979–82 developed as a housing estate; in 1982 the main workshops were all demolished, but one shed was left – that where the Ruston locomotives had been kept; this remnant was pulled down in February 1989. The standard gauge loco shed was marked only by the footings and the inspection pit. The adit and cutting were landscaped in a smooth grass-covered valley.

Another trackway from the road led to the locomotive shed area, more or less on the route of the one-time narrow gauge line and this course can be followed on the northwest side of Wellingborough Road into open fields, partly on an embankment – and even when at ground level the course can be discerned by differences in vegetation (in Spring there are fewer buttercups than in the surrounding field, for example). The top end is lost amongst later excavations associated with the cement works, and near White Lodge were some old quarries, with a subsidence hole above the underground workings at one point; but all this area was levelled in July 1984. The cement works area, however, undisturbed agriculturally for fifty years or so, developed an interesting flora and fauna that together with its geological features has made it of great interest to naturalists; and by arrangement with the landowners (the British Steel Corporation Pension Fund) the Nature Conservancy Council and the local authority have preserved it as a Site of Special Scientific Interest (*'Evening Telegraph'*, 18th July 1983).

Footnotes

1. *Indented Bar Bulletin* No. 51; Indented Bar & Concrete Engineering Co Ltd, April 1919. Thanks to Mr G.H. Starmer for this obscure item.
2. *Electric Traction Jubilee*, 1896–1946. J.H. Cansdale for BTH Ltd, December 1946, p.52. Thanks to Dr Iain D.O. Frew for this. See also *'The Narrow Gauge'* No. 92, p.28 – Dr Frew's note.
3. *Evening Telegraph*, 13th August 1920. Thanks to R.N. Sherwood for this.
4. *'The working of coal and other stratified minerals'*. H.F. Bulman, p.291. Benn 1927

Grid References

940699	Adit
940697	Locomotive sheds
935704	Terminus of overland tramway
940697	Workshops
940698	Diesel locomotive shed
941697	Wagon shops
942695	Kilns (west end)
936694	Reversing point on s.g. tramway
949695	Junction with LMSR
943696	Wall of tipping site

Locomotives

Connection to main line.

Gauge; 4ft 8½ins

MARY ANN	4-4-OT				?			(a)	Scr 1920
SUNSHINE	0-4-OST				?			(b)	s/s
28.No. 9	0-6-OST	OC	P	751	1898	14 x 20ins	3ft 7ins	(c)	Scr 8/1957
STEPHENSON	0-6-OST	IC	RS	2837	1896	14 x 20ins	3ft 6ins	(d)	Scr 4/1960
'FRANCE'	0-4-OST	OC	AB	1466	1916	14 x 22ins	3ft 5ins	(e)	Scr c 8/1965
HENRY CORT	0-4-OST	OC	P	933	1903	14 x 20ins	3ft 2ins	(f)	(1)
25 SIEMENS	0-4-OST	OC	EV	3	1909			(g)	(2)

(a)	ex ?, 1915
(b)	ex ?
(c)	ex Ebbw Vale Ironworks c 1925
(d)	ex Ebbw Vale Ironworks c 1935
(e)	ex Panteg Steelworks 4/1956
(f)	ex Blisworth Quarries 7/1957
(g)	ex Ebbw Vale Steelworks 2/1962

(1)	to Foxfield Light Railway Society, Dilhorne, Staffordshire 2/1967
(2)	to Blisworth Quarries 4/1966

White Lodge Quarries

Gauge; 3ft 0ins

–	0-4-OST	OC	HC	505	1898	9 x 15ins	2ft 3ins	(a)	s/s

(a)   ex J.F. Wake, dealer, Darlington, c. 1916. Orig. Newcastle & Gateshead Water Co. Some authorities quote the maker's number as 506

Irthlingborough Mines

Gauge; 3ft 0ins

1	4wWE	GEC/USA	6100	1916	25hp	7ton	New 1916 Scr 1966	
2	4wWE	GEC/USA	6099	1916	25hp	7ton	New 1916	(1)
3	4wWE	GB	1545	1938	80hp	8ton	New 5/1938	(2)
		Reb as 4wBE 1/1964						
4	4wWE	GB	1566	1938	80hp	8ton	New 7/1938	(2)
		Reb as 4wBE 12/1964						
5	4wWE	GB	1567	1938	80hp	8ton	New 8/1938	(2)
		Reb as 4wBE 3/1962						
6	4wWE	GB	1746	1941	80hp	8ton	New 8/1941	(2)
		Reb as 4wBE 7/1964						
1	4wBE	BEV	78	1919	2hp	2ton	New 3/1919	Scr 1966
2	4wBE	BEV	79	1919	2hp	2ton	New 3/1919	Scr 1966
3	4wBE	BEV	156	1919	2hp	2ton	New 11/1919	Scr 1966
4	4wBE	BEV	157	1920	2hp	2ton	New 2/1920	Scr 1966
5	4wBE	BEV	252	1920	2hp	2ton	New 5/1920	Scr c.10/1966
6	4wBE	BEV	253	1920	2hp	2ton	New 5/1920	Scr c 12/1966
7	4wBE	BEV	254	1920	2hp	2ton	New 8/1920	Scr c 10/1966
8	4wBE	BEV	255	1920	2hp	2ton	New 8/1920	Scr c 10/1966
9	4wBE	BEV	374	1922	2hp	2ton	New 1/1922	Scr c 12/1966
10	4wBE	BEV	375	1922	4.8hp	2ton	New 1/1922	Scr c 10/1966
11	4wBE	BEV	376	1922	4.8hp	2ton	New 1/1922	Scr 1966
12	4wBE	BEV	377	1922	2hp	2ton	New 1/1922	Scr c 12/1966
13	4wBE	BEV	378	1922	2hp	2ton	New 1/1922	Scr 1966
14	4wBE	BEV	379	1922	2hp	2ton	New 2/1922	Scr 1966
15	4wBE	Irthlingboro'		1938 (?)			New	Scr 1966
16	4wBE	Irthlingboro'		1938 (?)			New Scr c 12/1966	
69	4wBE	GB	1569	1938	4.5hp	3ton	New 7/1938	(2)
70.18	4wBE	GB	1570	1938	4.5hp	3ton	New 7/1938	(2)
71.20	4wBE	GB	1571	1938	4.5hp	3ton	New 8/1938	(2)
72.23	4wBE	GB	1572	1938	4.5hp	3ton	New 8/1938	(2)
73.24	4wBE	GB	1573	1938	4.5hp	3ton	New 9/1938	(2)

74	4wBE	GB	1574	1938	4.5hp	3ton	New 9/1938	(2)
61	4wBE	GB	2061	1947	4.5hp	3ton	New 7/1947	(2)
62	4wBE	GB	2062	1947	4.5hp	3ton	New 7/1947	(2)
63.22	4wBE	GB	2063	1947	4.5hp	3ton	New 7/1947	(2)
78	4wBE	GB	2078	1947	4.5hp	3ton	New 6/1947	(2)
79	4wBE	GB	2079	1947	4.5hp	3ton	New 6/1947	(2)
80	4wBE	GB	2080	1947	4.5hp	3ton	New 6/1947	(2)
91	4wBE	GB	2291	1950	4.5hp	3ton	New 6/1950	(2)
92.21	4wBE	GB	2292	1950	4.5hp	3ton	New 6/1950	(2)
93	4wBE	GB	2293	1950	4.5hp	3ton	New 6/1950	(2)
94.19	4wBE	GB	2294	1950	4.5hp	3ton	New 6/1950	(2)
95	4wBE	GB	2295	1950	4.5hp	3ton	New 6/1950	(2)
96.17	4wBE	GB	2296	1950	4.5hp	3ton	New 6/1950	(2)
Loco. No. 1	4wDM	RH	187074	1938	44/48HP class 6ton		New 1/1938	(2)
	4wDM	RH	187076	1938	44/48HP class 6ton		New 5/1938	(2)
3	4wDM	RH	418803	1957	48DLG class 7ton		(a)	(2)
4	4wDM	RH	353491	1953	LBU class (31.5hp) 3½ton		(a)	(2)
5	4wDM	RH	338439	1953	LBU class (31.5hp) 3½ton		(a)	(2)
6	4wDM	RH	375694	1954	LBU class (31.5hp) 3½ton		(a)	(2)
7	4wDM	RH	418764	1957	LBU class (31.5hp) 3½ton		(a)	(2)
8	4wDM	RH	427802	1958	LBU class (31.5hp) 3½ton		(a)	(2)
24	4wDM	RH	433388	1960	48DLG class 7ton		(b)	(2)
–	4wDM	RH	451900	1961	48DLG class 7ton		(c)	(2)

(a)   ex Dorman Long Ltd, Lingdale Mine, Cleveland, 1962
(b)   ex Dorman Long Ltd, Kilton Mine, Cleveland, c 1/1964
(c)   ex Dorman Long Ltd, LIngdale Mine, 1964

(1)   to W.J. Redden & Sons, Wellingborough for scrap 3/1966
(2)   to T.H. Sheppard & Sons Ltd, Wellingborough, for scrap 3/1967

Some of the 4wBE locomotives 1–16 may have changed numbers later.

Gauge; 2ft 6ins (locomotive stored for spares only)

4wDM	RH	375693	1954	LBU class (31½hp) 3½ton	(a)	(1)
4wDM	RH	338438	1953	LBU class (31½hp) 3½ton	(a)	(1)
4wDM	RH	418765	1957	LBU class (31½hp) 3½ton	(a)	(1)
4wDM	RH	353486	1953	LBU class (31½hp) 3½ton	(a)	(1)
4wDM	RH	375329	1954	48DLU class 7ton	(a)	(1)

(a)   ex Dorman Long Ltd, Kilton Mine, Cleveland 1964

(1)   to T.H. Sheppard & Sons Ltd, Wellingborough, for scrap 3/1967

Irthlingborough Mines.   The last train of ore leaves the mines on 30th September 1965. The general manager, Mr. W.E. Davies, is second from the right, and the tall man at his left is Mr. Knibbs, a RTB director.   B. Hales

Irthlingborough Mines.   The sealed mine entrance, late 1966. This has now been covered over and the whole site has been 'landscaped'.   A.J. Pack

WEST END OR IRTHLINGBOROUGH QUARRIES

Owners: Arthur Dunmore; Dunmore Ltd from 7th October 1898; Premier Portland Cement Co Ltd from 24th January 1907; British Portland Cement Manufacturers Ltd from 20th November 1911.

Arthur Dunmore of Central Farm, Irthlingborough developed several minerals on his land – clay for brickmaking, lime for cement manufacture, and ironstone, the last being quoted by LQ only for 1895/8, 1900/6, with the last entry under the style of Dunmore Ltd. A further change of ownership, with more specific aims, came about in 1907, whereafter cement manufacture was the prime concern, but ironstone was still occasionally sold, presumably being exposed during the course of quarrying for limestone, and was recorded in LQ for 1912/3.

The precise location of the earliest quarries is uncertain, but they were close to the Wellingborough road at the southwest end of Irthlingborough; the limestone quarries associated with the cement works were on the north side of the road, but the OS of 1924 shows a small disused quarry on the south side, immediately west of the stream, and it is possible that ironstone came initially from here, to be taken away by the standard gauge tramway that followed the streamside for a third of a mile before turning east towards the LNWR line. The siding agreement with the latter is dated 6th August 1897, suggesting that it had only been installed shortly before that. The tramway was taken under the main road to what became the cement works area, while the limestone quarry was served by a two-foot gauge tramway. The standard gauge line was operated by steam locomotives, for which a stone-built shed was provided about 150 yards south of the road; the roofless walls are still standing, and there are vague traces of the tramway down to the BR course. The bridge under the Wellingborough road has been filled in, and parts of the cement works remain in other hands; and there are extensive traces of the associated quarries. Part of the area north of White Lodge was in 1916 leased for ironstone mining by Ebbw Vale Steel Iron & Coal Co Ltd, as part of their Irthlingborough complex.

Grid Reference

938699	Standard gauge locomotive shed for cement works; quarry probably to northwest of this point

Locomotives

Gauge; 4ft 8½ins

0-6-OST	IC	MW 688	1878	12 x 17ins	3ft 1⅜ins	(a)	(1)
0-4-OST	OC	MW 952	1886	12 x 18ins	2ft 9ins	(b)	s/s

(a) ex T.A. Walker Ltd, contractors
(b) ex T. Mitchell & Sons Ltd, Bolton, 4/1901 (form. Connington, Shaw & Co Ltd, St Helens)

(1) to T. Mitchell & Sons Ltd, Bolton

IRTHLINGBOROUGH QUARRIES

Owners: Irthlingborough Iron Ore Co Ltd.

This company appears to have been the first to operate in Irthlingborough itself and was registered on 25th February 1890, one of the directors being John Spencer of the Manor House, Irthlingborough, and it was apparently mainly his land that was to be worked. The *'Wellingborough News'* of 14th March 1890 reports that a 'tramway is now being prepared'; this was a half-mile standard gauge line from the LNWR, the siding agreement being dated 28th August 1890, from a junction close to the bridge over the Nene, with the quarries on rising ground southeast of the main road, High St West. The exact extent of the line has escaped record, as the company was short-lived; if the standard gauge line reached the quarry area, the steep bank would almost certainly require a locomotive, but none are known to have been owned by the company; possibly a narrow gauge feeder was used between the working face and the standard gauge upper terminus – but this is conjecture.

The company was wound up in May 1898 and a new company was formed with the same title, only to be dissolved on 9th December 1902. Also in May 1898 the Irthlingborough Brick & Tile Co Ltd was formed, to work the area abandoned by the iron ore company, with permission to use the branch railway 'from dock to the LNWR' (perhaps implying that there **was** a tipping dock at the upper terminus). This company was wound up at the end of 1900. Finally, the site was acquired by Hatton Shaw & Co (Irthlingborough) Ltd, registered on 30th December 1913; they were tanners, but included brickmaking on the side. They too used the 'railroad', this time providing a 'locomotive' constructed from a road steam locomotive; but when Ebbw Vale came on the scene, using the same connection to the LNWR, they handled Hatton Shaw's traffic by arrangement, until the tramway closed about 1922. Latterly the line consisted of three tracks, the northernmost one being the original, still in position for most of its length until the 1950s. The quarry area was still visible in part by the sunken ground southeast of the main road on the north side of the trackway to the former Ebbw Vale plant, but in 1979 a new road for a housing estate was constructed on the site.

_# Irthlingborough Quarries (Irthlingborough Iron Ore)

Grid Reference

943699   Southwest corner of quarry area and possible site of tipping dock

Irthlingborough Quarries. The Irthlingborough Iron Co ceased quarrying about 1900 but the signal box retained its original name throughout, as here on 2nd September 1965, just four weeks before RTB closed their mines.   Ian L. Wright

THE NENE VALLEY GROUP

For the remaining quarries in this part we move to the valley of the Nene as the river makes its slow-moving way north-eastwards from Irchester to Thrapston. There were quarries on both sides, mostly with tramway connections to the LNWR Blisworth-Peterborough line that here hugged the river and avoided close contact with villages. The quality of the ore becomes progressively poorer further downstream, especially to the east; as a result, these pits were all short-lived, have left very few traces, and information about them is correspondingly meagre – but they were pleasantly situated, with sweeping views across the Nene valley, inviting the walker to explore.

CHELVESTON QUARRIES

Owners: Hunsbury Hill Iron Co (?); Thomas Butlin & Co Ltd from c.1889; Wellingborough Iron Co Ltd from 1930.

Ironstone and limestone, principally the latter, were obtained from these quarries, but their history is imperfectly known. MS reports ironstone from Chelveston for 1891/2 and LQ records limestone for 1902/3, but the pits were opened for some time before that, and the 1884 OS shows two tramways serving different quarries about two thirds of a mile apart. The southern quarry lay about half a mile east of Chelveston Lodge, and the tramway from it ran along the north side of a brook, to end by the road from Stanwick to Higham Ferrers; the northern quarries were on the west of the same road ('the upper road') a half mile north of Chelveston Lodge, with a tramway running westwards, again on the north side of a brook for part of the way, to end at a tipping dock on the Stanwick–Irthlingborough road ('the lower road'). The OS map shows limekilns near the quarry. The southern quarry was in the parish of Chelveston-cum-Caldecott, the northern one in Raunds parish, so possibly the ironstone came from the former; but with so little evidence we cannot be sure.

Additional information about these obscure workings came to light in 1987. In the course of research into the ironworks of Northamptonshire, Geoffrey Starmer came across a report of a meeting of the Irthlingborough District Highway Board in 1883, when the clerk reported that £75 had been received from the chairman of Hunsbury Hill Iron Co, in respect of extra traffic on the Stanwick road. Earlier that year, a local gentleman, Spencer Pratt Esq, had complained of the bad state of the roads in and about Stanwick "which was chiefly occasioned by the extra traffic from the iron pits; he had put up with it for two years and leases of the ironstone pits were for another 18 years". Another source of information appeared in the correspondence columns of the '*Evening Telegraph*' in September 1987, in letters from Ralph Thompson and A. George; the output of the quarries was moved by horsepower and gravity, with the brakesman applying a 'sprag' between the wheel spokes if necessary. From the road end the ore was conveyed by horse and cart to Irthlingborough station, where a ramp was provided so that the carts could tip their loads into railway wagons for transit to Butlin's furnaces at Wellingborough. The gauge of the tramways was said to be about 18 inches.

These accounts fill in nicely some of the detail lacking in MS; it seems that at first the quarries were owned by Hunsbury Hill Iron Co, with a 20-year lease from 1881, but that Butlin's took over the site before the expiry of the lease. It is not known when these quarries were closed but probably early in the present century. Hewlett states that in 1930 Wellingborough Iron Co Ltd obtained a lease to work limestone from the Stanwick area, using lorries between quarries and Wellingborough works.

On the southern tramway, the quarrying site is still visible as a flattened area below the level of the surrounding fields, but of the almost level tramway one mile in length there is no trace at all. At the road end the roadside ditch emptying into the stream is covered over for about fifteen yards, perhaps where the carts entered the field for loading from the tramway.

Ore from the northern quarries is stated by a local man to have been carried in tubs of one ton capacity, hauled by horses; the line descends almost a hundred feet (210 O.D. to 115 O.D.) in its course to the tipping dock about two thirds of a mile away, so was more difficult to work than the one already described, and there are more interesting remains of it. East of the Stanwick–Higham Ferrers road is a wide area of shallow pits from which limestone has been extracted, and in 1979 in process of being filled with rubbish; these presumably represent the Wellingborough Iron

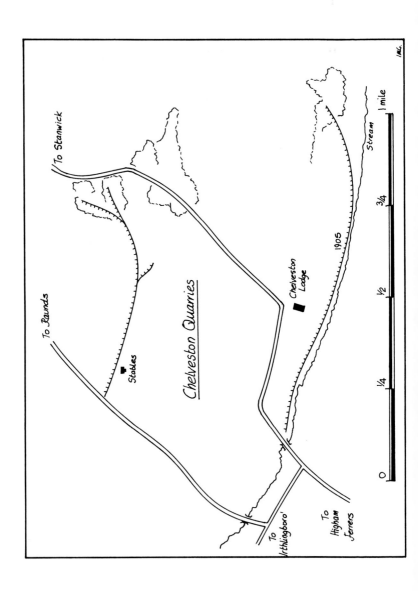

Chelveston Quarries.   Transport from these quarries was unusual in that the first part of the journey was by horse haulage over a narrow gauge tramway ending at a tipping dock by the Irthlingborough–Stanwick road. The ore was then carted to Irthlingborough LNWR station about half a mile away. The picture shows the tipping dock, at the rear of which can be glimpsed the stable for the horses. 8th October 1987.   Eric Tonks

Co's workings, as they appear to be relatively recent, and are not shown on the early maps. West of the road are two much older quarries, both now occupied by private houses (one is named 'The Quarry'): the tramway from these ran across the fields at a gentle gradient and ended at the Stanwick–Irthlingborough road, where today can be seen the remains of an elevated tipping dock and a set of brick-built stables nearby, isolated from any existing farm buildings. They were still there in 1987.

Grid References

968707	Stables near tipping dock
967708	Tipping dock on Stanwick–Irthlingborough road
966700	Tipping dock on Stanwick–Higham Ferrers road
976708	Quarry area (west end)
978697	Quarry area (west end) – Chelveston Lodge

RINGSTEAD QUARRIES

Owners: Butlin Bevan & Co; Butlin Bevan & Co Ltd from 27th June 1889.

Whilst traces of Walters' Addington quarries and tramway are still obvious, there are practically none to be seen of Butlin's system. Production commenced in November 1871 (*Mining Journal*, 11th November 1872, p 1002) and in his *'History of Northamptonshire'* (1874, p 905) Whellan records an output of a thousand tons per week – quite substantial for the time. The OS for 1883 shows a number of standard gauge sidings at Ringstead & Addington Halt, and from them a narrow gauge tramway running from a point alongside one of them to the quarries about half a mile to the southeast, on the higher ground overlooking the station. Horses provided the motive power and side-tipping wagons may be presumed to have been used; the ore is said to have been calcined, probably near the LNWR line, along which it was subsequently taken to the ironworks. Production ceased in 1891 and the system was dismantled, and there are few traces today; the bridleway to the deserted village of Mallows Cotton crosses the tramway route and on the eastern side the ground is noticeably lower than the hedge at one point. But it is worth a visit; the picturesque footpath from Great Addington has stepping stones at the river crossing, and these shaped blocks of granite, sandstone and limestone, are probably of railway origin.

Grid Reference

970743   Tipping dock to LNWR

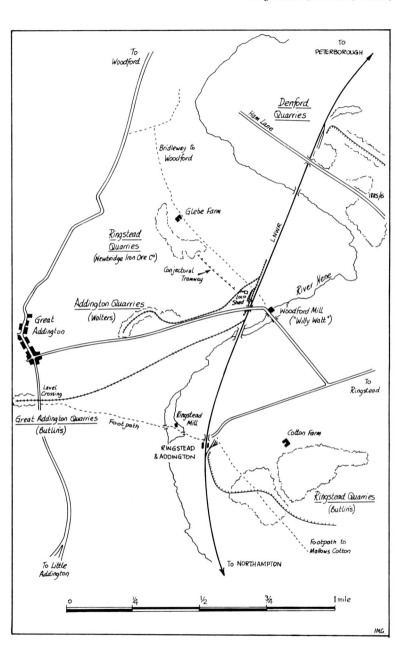

GREAT ADDINGTON QUARRIES

Owners: Butlin Bevan & Co; Thomas Butlin & Co Ltd from 27th June 1889.

As with other workings in the vicinity, there is very little information to be had about those at Great Addington. MS records output only for the years 1891/2, but it is possible that the output for earlier years was combined with that from Ringstead; and the OS for 1883 does not show any tramway. Mr Peck, whose personal recollections form the substance of this account, stated that the system lasted about fifteen years, being closed at the turn of the century or a few years later. The purchase of a new locomotive numbered 1 (Butlin Bevan only had two locomotives as far as is known) in 1884 suggests this date as the possible opening of the tramway, i.e. with the locomotive as ordered.

Of the course of the line there is little doubt, in spite of the almost complete lack of any remains today, as it followed the course of the stream down to the LNWR. It crossed the main street of Great Addington village by a gated level crossing, on the eastern side of which was the locomotive shed, and on the other were the pits. The line had a gentle slope with the load for most of its three-quarter mile length and on one occasion there was a runaway, when one employee had the presence of mind to open the gates in readiness!.. fortunately, no serious damage was done.

In the 1950's the trackbed just east of the level crossing was still traceable for a short distance, and the working face was visible, but by 1987 these slender traces had vanished and it was even difficult to identify the site of the level crossing. A patch of rough ground by the footpath to the Finedon road is at the site of the quarry. Much of the tramway route to the LNWR line has been quarried for gravel in recent years, leaving the usual pattern of flooded ground. There is virtually nothing to be seen at the LNWR end and it is difficult to see how the siding was accommodated, though the OS shows a siding under the eastern railway arch; possibly there has been some slipping of the embankment.

Grid References

972752	Junction with LNWR
959747	Level crossing
959747	Quarry face

Locomotive

Gauge: 4ft 8½ins

No. 1 JOE   0-4-OST   CC   HC   252   1884 13 x 20ins   3ft 6ins   New 1/1884   s/s

ADDINGTON QUARRIES

Owner: Thomas Walters

The LNWR line from Wellingborough to Thrapston crossed the meandering and slowly-flowing Nene no less than eight times and on two of the intervening spurs of high ground, at this point a mere hundred feet or so above sea level, beds of iron ore were worked at an early date. The Addington quarries, though shorter lived than Butlin's Ringstead quarries, have left more obvious traces in the form of a cutting along the crest of the low hill where the pits were situated. While traces of these workings are still to be seen, some doubt surrounds their history because of the difficulty in interpreting the entries in MS, which records Newbridge Iron Ore Co as operating quarries at Ringstead in 1873–81, closed in 1882, and Thomas Walters operating at Addington, Ringstead 1881–4, disused 1885. The 'Ringstead' of these references means that the ore was placed on the LNWR near to Ringstead & Addington station, a wayside halt very much in open country and a long way from either village. Neither of the quarries were in Ringstead parish. The site of Walters' quarry is amply confirmed by the OS and present-day remains, but that of the Newbridge quarries was far more difficult to establish. *Kelly's Directory* for 1890 quotes Thomas Walters as having worked quarries at Great Addington, opened in 1877 and 'not now in use'. Thomas Walters was a bailiff and is believed to have had some associations with Great Addington Hall. It seems likely, therefore that quarrying commenced in 1877 rather than 1881.

The worked area lay on the north side of the road from Great Addington to Ringstead, west of the railway, to which it was connected by a standard gauge tramway with a sharp descent at the railway end. The 6ins OS shows a locomotive shed but the only clue to the identity of the occupant is that provided by the advertisement in the *'Colliery Guardian'* when the quarries were closed in 1885. This suggests that the locomotive for disposal was RAUNDS from the nearby quarries of that name; which if so means that the quarries were without a locomotive before about 1883, or there was an unidentified earlier engine. The steepness of the gradient up from the LNWR suggests the latter as more likely.

When work ceased in 1885 the tramway was dismantled but the quarries were evidently left as they were, with no attempt at restoration, and they remained thus until about 1970, when there was a general levelling of the worked area for agricultural use. As a result, only a small upper portion of the final working face is now exposed, but the course of the tramway is still clear as a bushy gullet where it runs close to the road. The section from here down to the LNWR has been filled in and the thicket where the locomotive shed used to stand has been removed; at the railway end the ground includes an area of deep red dust indicative of calcining.

Grid References

973753	Junction with LNWR
972753	Locomotive shed
965750	Terminus of tramway

Locomotive

Gauge; 4ft 8½ins

RAUNDS   0-4-0ST   OC   HC   219   1881 14 x 20ins   3ft 6½ins   (a)   (1)

(a)   ex Raunds Quarries c 1883

(1)   to Stanton Ironworks Co Ltd

The identity of this locomotive is presumed

RINGSTEAD QUARRIES

Owners: Newbridge Iron Ore Co.

We have adopted the title 'Ringstead Quarries' because this is the only one to appear in known published references, all taking their cue from the original entry in MS. This source lists Thomas Walters' quarry as 'Addington, Ringstead', with the Addington location confirmed by the 1884 OS; but there is no similar amplification for Newbridge Iron Ore Co (listed as operating 1873–81) and nothing is shown on the OS, so the site of these workings remained undetermined. We had long ago realised that the 'Ringstead' referred to the nearest station to where the ore was put on the railway, and that the quarries were in the vicinity but not necessarily in the parish. For further progress we had to hope that more documents might be found, and this was realised in 1987, thanks – as so often in these difficult cases – to the help of local historians. The vital reference is on page 138 of *'Woodford juxta Thrapston'* by Eric and Mary Humphries (Buscott Publications, 1985), brought to our notice through the kindness of Dick Berridge (former digger driver at Islip quarries, who lived in Woodford and is the possessor of a great fund of knowledge of the local quarries) and Greg Evans, a younger historian who has contributed so much in recent years. Dr Humphries has also provided greater detail on the areas covered. We are grateful to them all.

In Northamptonshire Record Office is a draft, dated 10th December 1873, of a lease between Appleby & Co, proprietors of Renishaw Ironworks, near Chesterfield, and the Rev. Christopher Smyth, Rector of Woodford, for nearly three acres of Top Mill Way, on the north side of the Addington–Ringstead road close to Woodford Mill. The land was required for tramways and buildings associated with ironstone quarrying, for a term of 31 years, and a wayleave of ½d per ton was to be levied on ore travelling over the land from areas other than Rectory Farm or Woodford Mill. This established that the transfer to the LNWR was the same as that used by Addington Quarries, owned by Thomas Walters, who was connected with Newbridge Iron Ore Co, which was a subsidiary of Appleby & Co. The clear indication of Rectory Farm as the site of the quarry was confirmed by an early Geological Survey map in the archives of B S C, Corby (thanks to Norman Bellamy, surveyor, for this equally vital document); the field to the west of Glebe Farm, alias Rectory Farm, is shown to have been quarried, and the site can still (1987) be seen; the swathe in the land west of the farm buildings and – more tellingly – two dips in front of the hedge where the ironstone face came close to the field edge. As tramways feature in the draft lease, there would presumably have been one to Rectory Farm, but after a century of ploughing it is hardly surprising that no traces remain; probably of narrow gauge, it might have been alongside the present-day bridleway, which stands above the general field level. It was lifted very soon after closure of the quarry, as nothing appears on the 1884 OS.

Grid References

969755	Site of quarry face by hedge
968757	Quarry site west of Glebe Farm

Addington Quarries. The quarries in the Addington–Ringstead area provided many puzzles in the elucidation of their history. They were all small and short-lived and few appear on OS maps. Our picture is of the only one to leave recognisable remains; the curved ironstone face lies alongside the road from Addington to Ringstead, on the north side. The area in the foreground, once quarried, has been levelled and the original gullet in front of the face has been brought to the same level. 7th March 1978. Eric Tonks

DENFORD QUARRIES

Owners: Glendon Iron Co (?)

The only quarries listed under this title in output statistics date from World War I (see the next section) but there were earlier workings here; the difficulty lies in deciding ownership. The 1884 OS map shows a siding on the LNWR here but no quarry or tramway, and the LNWR working timetable for November 1886 refers to this as 'Woodford Siding'; the site is about equidistant from Ringstead and Denford. This LNWR information was kindly provided by Mr A.St.G. Walsh. In the Northamptonshire Record Office there is a note of a field 'bordering the railway line at Denford, a portion of which has been taken by the Glendon Iron Co as at March 1885', and NSI refer to workings here 'before 1899', presumably basing their deductions on the OS map of that date; and the existing traces in the vicinity of Ham Lane seem far more likely to go back to the 19th century than World War I.

Our knowledge of these early workings is confined to these traces on the ground. NSI refers to workings a quarter mile southeast of Ham Lane bridge, south of the lane, but the visible traces are on the north side of the lane at this point, and include an area of shallow stone covering a few fields, probably served by a narrow gauge tramway running to the LNWR siding at a presumed tipping dock; or there may have been a standard gauge siding, as Glendon Iron Co usually preferred. Haulage would probably be by horses or by hand.

No record survives of the period of operation, or to indicate that it was ever worked fully at all, but in the vicinity of Ham Lane, which crossed the BR line to the south, there are two old gullets still visible, as indicated on the 6ins OS; they lie outside the area purchased by Keeble (see next section) and this almost certainly must be associated with the earlier phase of operation. The area was opened up again on a more ambitious (though unfulfilled) scale just before World War I, as described below.

DENFORD QUARRIES

Owners: G. Keeble and E.M. Jellett; R.E. Campbell from 1st October 1914; Ebbw Vale Steel, Iron & Coal Co Ltd from 9th November 1915; Richard Thomas & Co Ltd from 3rd April 1936.

Just before World War I, George Keeble and E.M. Jellett prospected the area between Wellingborough and Thrapston with the aim of opening up suitable sites for ironstone working; of these, Finedon Park has already been described, and the present pits represent a less successful venture. In 1912 the partners purchased an area of 296 acres extending from the LNWR between Ham Lane and the river Nene bridge to the north, eastwards for about 1¼ miles, south of Denford village, to within a hundred yards or so of the Midland Rly Kettering–Huntingdon line. The LNWR siding was in Ringstead parish, but most of the ground was in Denford parish. The old 'Woodford Siding' here had presumably been removed, and a new and extended layout provided under the title 'Keeble's Siding'. This was under construction late in 1912, and it was hoped to send out about 300 tons of ore per day. (*'Kettering Leader'*, 22nd November 1912).

The main workings lay about a third of a mile west of Denford, on flattish ground near the river and at just over the 100-foot datum represent the lowest level at which Northampton Sand ironstone has been worked. They were served by a narrow gauge tramway leading to an elevated tipping dock alongside a siding from the LNWR; there is doubt as to the gauge, but it seems probable from the LNWR siding diagram that the system consisted of light 2ft gauge Jubilee (or Decauville) track, with end-tipping wooden wagons that were hauled by horses. There was also a branch tramway towards Ham Lane.

Production commenced in 1913, according to MS, and after a year in the ownership of R.E. Campbell, the site was taken over by Ebbw Vale, along with the Finedon Park property. Ebbw Vale did some prospecting, driving a gullet some six hundred yards long; but the ore was found to be very siliceous, and work soon stopped about 1917 or 1918 – and the track was removed. The Ebbw Vale company leased the terminal gullet for five years from 1st January 1932 to Thrapston RDC for the deposit of refuse – one of the earliest recorded cases of this kind of ironstone quarry 'restoration'. Richard Thomas acquired the property along with the rest of Ebbw Vale's land in 1936 but no further work was done, and the land was sold.

The embankment supporting the tramway was still extant up to 1960, and possibly up to 1977; a visit in April 1978 revealed that this area near the site of the BR line had very recently been 'gone over' by earthmoving equipment that had obliterated the embankment completely and smoothed over the land (which still had a lot of ironstone lumps on the surface to show its origin). At the BR hedge the ground was raised almost on a platform of ironstone. The visible gullet near Ham Lane belongs to the earlier period of working (see above).

Grid References

977763	Junction with LNWR/Tipping dock
977760	Gullet on north side of Ham Lane (south end)
980761	Tramway embankment

THRAPSTON QUARRIES

Owners: Thomas Whitehouse; Thrapston Iron Ore Co Ltd from 1875.

These pits, very much on the edge of the workable ironstone field, were opened up in 1873, and a standard gauge line was constructed to them from a siding in Thrapston MR station. Horse traction is believed to have been used, but there is virtually no information on the quarries, which were closed in May 1881, according to MS. The stone would almost certainly have been very siliceous, so a short life is hardly surprising; however, the site was acquired by the Glendon Iron Co in 1881, but for limestone only, which was worked up to 1900, according to plans deposited in the Northamptonshire Record Office. Thrapstone Iron Ore Co Ltd was officially wound up on 15th June 1883, according to *'Mechanical World and Steam Users Journal'*, XV, 20th July 1883, p 258. Thanks are due to Gordon Green for this obscure item.

The track was lifted at an unknown date, but the site was reopened in 1933 for the quarrying of limestone, and light 1ft 11½ins gauge track was laid over the route of the former ironstone tramway. A little later a further line at a higher level and at right angles to it ended at a tipping stage over the lower line. Intermediate trans-shipment between two lines of the same gauge is most unusual and hardly economic! These quarries also had a precarious existence under different owners and were closed in 1939. Part of the site was occupied in World War II by a rubber reclamation depot, which was dismantled later to leave the quarries much as their previous owners had abandoned them – including track, skips, and two petrol locomotives – only more overgrown. The locomotives were cut up in the middle 1950s but much of the rest was left, and by 1985 the area was a rough playground, worth a visit for the sake of discovering all sorts of forgotten relics – the grading plant, asphalt plant, the old tipping dock to the main line siding, and some wagon frames. There is also a very nice limestone face, and a suggestion that the upper levels were used for obtaining ganister. There are almost no traces of ironstone quarrying, however!

About a third of a mile to the north is another quarry, indicated as for ironstone on a geological map in the BSC Regional Property Dept. This quarry lies at the rear of Neneside Ironworks, established in 1857 for the manufacture of agricultural implements, and the site is still (1989) in the rough state left after the cessation of work. The history of this undoubtedly early working is not known.

Grid References

996778	Junction with MR
998780	Terminus of tramway (north)
997777	Exchange point between n.g. lines (later)
996783	Quarry behind Neneside Ironworks

Thrapston Quarries. These quarries produced limestone mostly and had a chequered history extending up to World War II. We include this view, taken on 23rd April 1988, just because it shows the remains of 2ft gauge track and wagons. A.J. Cocklin

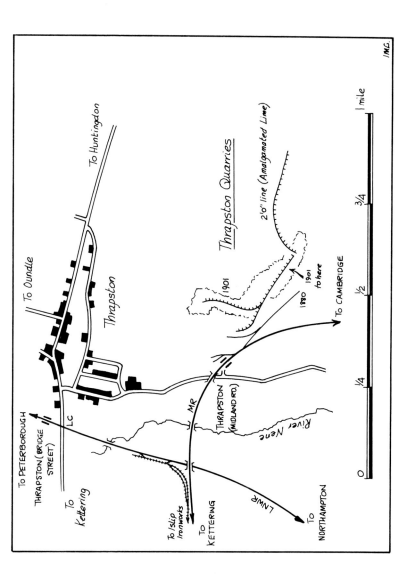

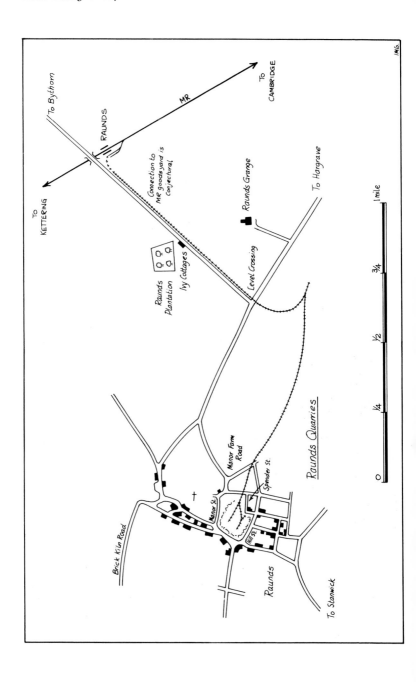

RAUNDS QUARRIES

Owners: Raunds Iron and Limestone Quarries Co Ltd; East Northamptonshire Ironstone Co Ltd from 5th April 1882.

The stroller down the main throughfare in Raunds, a small township of the Nene valley, will observe on one side a rockface of consideravle depth and of obviously ferruginous nature, and may speculate whether this selfsame outcrop stimulated the enterprise of the promoters of the 'Raunds Iron etc Co' (as it is referred to in MS). Maybe it was so; the stone looks rich enough – an appearance belied, alas, by results, as operations ceased after less than two years. Preliminary work to open ground on land belonging to John Pentelow of the Manor House began in November 1878[1] and the company, formed by Wallace Pedder and John Parkinson, was registered 24th December 1878.[2]

The quarries lay east of Raunds and were connected to the Midland Railway at Raunds station by a tramway nearly two miles in length, since the station, on the Kettering–Cambridge line, was this distance from the town it was supposed to serve. At a meeting of ratepayers in June 1879[3] there was a proposal on Mr Pedder's behalf to use steam traction along Keystone Road (later called Station Road), and in return for this privilege, granted in November 1878, he offered to run a passenger service. This probably explains the choice of standard gauge and 60 lb. bullhead rail in chairs for the track. The line traversed only flat country, bristling with level crossings, and about half way along included a reversal, the purpose ôf which is not clear; possibly an easternwards extension (for limestone?) to further working areas was contemplated. Along Keystone Road, leading to Raunds station, the line became a roadside tramway, but even here it hopped across from one side to the other to avoid cottages near the junction, and finally entered the station yard from behind the 'Railway Inn'. This information on the roadside line comes from Mr T.C.Smith, Managing Director of Raunds Brickworks Ltd, who had it from a very old inhabitant who saw the rail in position.

The line was under construction in May 1880 'from the works at the rear of the National Schools through Mr John Pentelow's fields to the Midland Railway station',[4] the owners being quoted as 'Raunds Iron Ore Co'; no two sources seem to use the same name! The line was opened on 3rd December 1880,[5] with the first record of output appearing in MS for 1881, and the solitary locomotive – purchased new from Hudswell

Clarke, emphasising that the company believed in doing things properly – arrived in February 1881. If there was any production before this, possibly a contractor's locomotive did the haulage. There is no record of any passenger service.

Raunds is right on the eastern limit of commercially workable ironstone, and the ore was probably too highly siliceous to be acceptable. Early in 1882 the company went into voluntary liquidation, probably as a result of the heavy capital expenditure and poor sales. However, the properties were taken over under the terms of an agreement dated 9th March 1882 by the East Northamptonshire Ironstone Co Ltd, described as a reconstruction of the Raunds Iron and Limestone Co Ltd, and was registered on 5th April 1882.[6] No output record under this name appears in MS, so it seems likely that they never got the place going again, and just over a year later, on 3rd July 1883, the Raunds Estates came under the auctioneer's hammer at the White Hart Hotel, Thrapston. This was under the will of John Pentelow, deceased, and the auctioneer was F.S.Abbott.[7] Most of the effects were of interest only to the agricultural community, but the prospectus stated that there were 'continuous beds of rich ironstone and limestone, with a tramway already constructed over the bulk of the Estate' and that 'Blast furnaces might with great advantage be constructed near the railway'. No doubt they had Islip in mind in making this suggestion, but the ore would never have been good enough. The tramway was described as 'nearly one mile long, with offices, weighing room and other buildings'; presumably this length of line would only include that on the Estate itself, south of the Hargrave road, and omit the roadside line. The 1884 OS shows the tramway ending south of the Hargrave road, and this probably represents the track referred to in the auctioneer's statement; the survey was done in 1884, i.e. in the period of lifting, not of construction. Possibly the estate took over the track on its own land under the terms of the lease, as was often the case. Needless to say, there were no takers in the ironstone industry, but the remaining track (or some of it, at any rate) was left in place; Mr York, security officer at Wellingborough Foundries in 1979, recalls seeing track in the fields when he was a boy, in the 1920–30 period, but not along the roadside, thus confirming the evidence of the OS map. Presumably it was lifted later, or just buried.

We have commented on the selection of standard gauge for this tramway, and we wonder if the promoters of the Kettering–Huntington line (who were very well aware of the potential ironstone traffic) encouraged these connections at Raunds, Thrapston, Barton Seagrave and Burton Latimer. A problem for the railway historian! The headquarters at Raunds are now occupied by 'Ponds Close' and the adjacent quarrying area is built over; there is no sign on the level crossing on Park Road, and the ground to the east was being cleared for more building in 1979. Beyond that is flat agricultural land upon which no traces remain, nor are there any along Station Road, where both verges are fairly wide. Raunds station is now a private residence. Today it is hard to believe that a tramway ever existed.

Footnotes

1. *Northampton Mercury*, 23rd November 1878
2. *Colliery Guardian*, 10th January 1879
3. *Northampton Mercury*, 28th June 1879
Thanks to Geoffrey Starmer for this and reference 1.
4. *Wellingborough News*, 15th May 1880; thanks to Russell Wear for this.
5. *Mining Journal*, 11th December 1880.
6. *Iron*, Vol 19, p 232. 28th April 1882.
7. *Iron*, Vol 21, p 549. 22nd June 1883.
Thanks to Gordon Green for these references.

Grid References

000728	Park Road crossing
003727	Manor Farm Road crossing
013724	Reversing point on tramway
012727	Level crossing of Hargrave Road
020736	Junction with MR

Locomotive

Gauge; 4ft 8½ins

RAUNDS   0-4-0ST   OC   HC   219   1881 14x20ins   3ft 6½ins   New 2/1881   (1)

(1)   to Thos Walters, Addington Quarries (?) c 1883

EXPLANATION OF TABLES

Locomotiuves

The columns show in order:– title: type: cylinder position: maker: maker's number: year built: cylinder dimensions: driving wheel diameter: origin: disposal. In referring to these columns the following points should be noted.

Title. Unofficial names used by the staff but not carried by the engine are denoted by inverted commas.

Type. The Whyte system of wheel classification is used, but if wheels are not connected by outside rods they are shown as 4w, 6w as the case may be.The following abbreviations are used:

T	Side Tank	DM	Diesel Mechanical	BE	Battery Electric
PT	Pannier Tank	DE	Diesel Electric	WE	Wire Electric
ST	Saddle Tank	DH	Diesel Hydraulic		
WT	Well Tank	PM	Petrol Mechanical		
VB	Vertical Boiler	PE	Petrol Electric		
G	Geared	PMR	Petrol Mechanical Railcar		

Cylinder Position		IC	Inside Cylinders
		OC	Outside Cylinders
		VC	Vertical Cylinders

Makers. The following abbreviations are used, with lesser known builders' names being given in full:

AB	Andrew Barclay Sons & Co Ltd, Kilmarnock
AE	Avonside Engine Co Ltd, Bristol
AP	Aveling & Porter Ltd, Rochester
B	Barclays & Co, Kilmarnock
BEV	British Electric Vehicles Ltd. Southport
Bg	E E. Baguley Ltd, Burton on Trent
BH	Black Hawthorn & Co Ltd. Gateshead
Bton	Brighton Locomotive Works, LB&SCR
CF	Chapman & Furneaux Ltd, Gateshead
DC	Drewry Car Co Ltd, London (Suppliers only)
DK	Dick, Kerr & Co Ltd, Preston
EE	English Electric Co Ltd, Preston
EV	Ebbw Vale Steel Coal & Iron Co Ltd, Ebbw Vale
FE	Falcon Engine & Car Works Ltd, Loughborough
FH	F. C. Hibberd & Co Ltd, London
FW	Fox Walker & Co Bristol
GB	Greenwood & Batley Ltd, Leeds
GEC/USA	General Electric Co, USA

H	James & Frederick Howard Ltd, Bedford
HC	Hudswell Clarke & Co Ltd, Leeds
HCR	Hudswell Clarke & Rodgers. Leeds
HE	Hunslet Engine Co Ltd, Leeds
HL	Hawthorn Leslie & Co Ltd, Newcastle upon Tyne
Hu	Robert Hudson Ltd, Leeds
JF	John Fowler & Co (Leeds) Ltd
K	Kitson & Co Ltd, Leeds
KE	Kilmarnock Engineering Co Ltd
KS	Kerr, Stuart & Co Ltd, Stoke on Trent
Mkm	Markham & Co Ltd, Chesterfield
MR	Motor Rail Ltd, Bedford
MW	Manning Wardle & Co Ltd, Leeds
N	Neilson & Co, Glasgow
OK	Orenstein & Koppel AG, Berlin
P	Peckett & Sons Ltd, Bristol
RH	Ruston & Hornsby Ltd, Lincoln
RR	Rolls Royce Ltd, Shrewsbury
RS	Robert Stephenson & Co Ltd, Newcastle upon Tyne and Darlington
RSH	Robert Stephenson & Hawthorns Ltd, Newcastle upon Tyne
S	Sentinel (Shrewsbury) Ltd
Sdn	Swindon Locomotive Works, GWR
SS	Sharp Stewart & Co Ltd, Glasgow
VF	Vulcan Foundry Ltd. Newton-le-Willows
WB	W. G. Bagnall Ltd, Stafford
YE	Yorkshire Engine Co Ltd, Sheffield

Maker's Number. Reb = Rebuilt.

Year Built. The year quoted is that given on the maker's plate, or from the maker's records if the date does not appear on the plate.

Cylinder and Driving Wheel Dimensions. These apply to locomotive as new.

Origin. 'New' indicates that the locomotive was delivered by the makers to this location at the stated date (to the month where known). Transfers from elsewhere are indicated by a bracketed letter and appropriate footnote.

Disposal.. Locomotives transferred to another owner or site are shown by a bracketed number with corresponding footnote. Scr = Scrapped. s/s = scrapped or sold, disposal unknown.

Quarry Machines

The information is set out in much the same way as for locomotives, but as collected information on quarry machines has not appeared before we give rather more in the way of explanation. The columns show in order:- title (if any): class description: power source and type of machine: maker: maker's number: year built: bucket capacity: jib or boom length: origin: disposal.

Title. Often machines carried no title. but major operators such as Stewarts & Lloyds Minerals Ltd gave them numbers, quoted where known; and a very few were named.

Class Description. Steam machines were most commonly referred to as '10 ton', '20-ton', etc, the 'ton' referring not to the weight but to the cutting pressure on the bucket teeth. Ruston Proctor & Co Ltd adopted these as class numbers, a No. 20 machine being a '20-ton' and so on, and these class numbers have been used in the tables, as in the manufacturer's literature. Whitaker's used a letter code but unfortunately only in a few cases do we know these. so we have had to fall back on '12-ton' etc. Ruston & Hornsby Ltd used designatory numbers for larger machines, e.g. No. 250.

Diesel and electric machines were given class numbers by Ruston Bucyrus Ltd from a scheme used by the Bucyrus Co. The early machines were described as 37B, 43B etc but this was later changed to 37RB and 43RB etc, and we have used the latter throughout lor simplicity. The numbers correspond roughly with the wieight of the machine in tons. Ransomes & Rapier Ltd applied class numbers such as 422, 480 etc, and also used these numbers for steam machines of the same power. The large Walking Draglines of both manufacturers incorporated 'W' in the class description – 3W, 5W for RB in ascending order of size, and W 150, W 1400 etc for R&R, the numbers again corresponding roughly to the weights.

Power Source and Type of Machine. The power source is indicated by a letter: S – Steam: D – Diesel. DE – Diesel Electric: E – Electric. PP – Petrol-paraffin.

The two main types of machine are shovels and draglines. In simple terms, the latter were used primarily tor removing overburden by dragging the bucket up the working face by a chain in a scraping motion, then slewing the bucket round to dump the load on the worked-out area; a shovel would then dig out the ore beneath. Obviously there are many variants on these according to circumstances, and digger drivers were very adept in using their machines in difficult positions. Some removal of overburden was done by 'stripping shovels' of large size. The form and duties of various specialized machines will be obvious from their names – crane. clamshell. back-acter, etc. Some machines were rail-mounted, some on crawlers or 'Caterpillar' tracks. When the type of machine is uncertain. the term 'navvy' is used.

Makers. The following abbreviations are used, with lesser known builder's narnes being given in full.

At	Atlantic Equipment Co, USA
BE	Bucyrus-Erie Co, USA
Berry	Henry Berry & Co Ltd, Leeds
Bu	Bucyrus Co, USA
Lima	Baldwin Lima Hamilton Co, USA
Marion	Marion Steam Shovel Co, USA
NBM	Newton, Bean & Mitchell, Bradford
Priestman	Priestman Brothers Ltd, Hull
RB	Ruston Bucyrus Ltd, Lincoln

RH	Ruston &: Hornsby Ltd, Lincoln
RP	Ruston Proctor & Co Ltd, Lincoln
R&R	Ransomes & Rapier Ltd, Ipswich
S&P	Stothert & Pitt Ltd, Bath
Taylor Hubbard	Taylor Hubbard & Co Ltd, Leicester
Wh	Whitaker Bros Ltd, Leeds
Wilson	John H. Wilson & Co Ltd, Liverpool

Makers' Number and **Year Built.** These are taken from manufacturers' records in the case of the Ruston companies and from R & R; from operators' records otherwise.

Bucket Capacity and **Jib or Boom Length.** The figures come from operators' records mostly, sometimes from manufacturers. There is no hard and fast rule about the terms 'jib' and 'boom' but generally steam machines are spoken of as having jibs, and diesel and electric machines booms, particularly the larger machines.

Origin. 'New' means that the machine was supplied by the makers to this location. The months quoted are those shown as delivery dates in the makers' records; but very often machines were supplied in sections to be assembled on site (this being particularly so with large machines) so that some time elapsed before they entered service. Transfers from other locations are shown by bracketed letters and appropriate footnotes. To save space, these footnotes also include details of any changes in bucket capacity or jib length.

Disposal. A machine transferred to another location is shown by a bracketed number and corresponding footnote Scr = scrapped- s/s = scrapped or sold, disposal unknown. These footnotes also include known details of the individual quarries or working faces that the machine served in the system concerned, with dates where known

Sources of Information. The principal sources of information consulted and quoted from, using the abbreviations given, are as follows. All were published by Her/His Majesty's Stationery Office.

Mineral Statistics of Great Britain. Robert Hunt	1853–81	(MS)
Mineral Statistics of Great Britain. Geological Survey Memoirs	1882–94	(MS)
List of Quarries in the United Kingdom and the Isle of Man	1895–1934	(LQ)
Special Reports on the Mineral Resources of Great Britain:		
Part XII – Iron Ore. Geological Survey Memoirs	1920	(GSM)
The Mesozoic Ironstone of England: The Northampton		
Sand Ironstone	1951	(NSI)
The Mesozoic Ironstone of England: The Liassic Ironstones	1952	(LI)

Wellingborough Quarries and Mines. 30HP Ruston Hornsby locomotive in Thingdon mine, c1934. Note the old rail and sleepers used for supporting the roof.

Ruston & Hornsby

INDEX

Irthlingborough Mines. A rare picture, showing the two types of trolley locomotive. Nos. 1 and 2 (see text for discussion on their curious history) are coupled together at the head of a heavy train from the mines (note wagons with built-up sides) while one of the GB series stands at right, 7th June 1958. Note the 'Safety First' sign over the tunnel entrance.

J.A. Peden

THE IRONSTONE QUARRIES OF THE MIDLANDS
HISTORY, OPERATION AND RAILWAYS
by Eric Tonks

This is a major authoritative work in several volumes on the ironstone industry of the Midlands, with particular emphasis on the railway and tramway systems. All parts are exceptionally well written with many photographs, superb maps of the systems, together with comprehensive locomotive and quarry machine details.

The parts published to date and the next part to be published (part 8) are detailed here.

PART ONE – INTRODUCTION
152 pages   109 b/w photographs   3 maps
1 870754 01 8   £12.95

This part tells in outline the history of the industry, its place in the economy, and its effect on the countryside; describes how the quarries were developed, operated and equipped; lists the sources of information used in the preparation of this and subsequent parts; and concludes with a chronology of all known quarries.

PART TWO – THE OXFORDSHIRE FIELD
252 pages   116 b/w photographs   15 maps
1 870754 02 6   £15.00

All ironstone quarries in Oxfordshire, the two in Warwickshire and a small group in the southern tip of Northamptonshire are described in detail in this book. Special attention is given to transport that played so vital a role in the industry; locomotives are fully described and listed, as too are the quarry machines – the diggers and draglines that replaced the hand labour of the early years.

PART THREE – THE NORTHAMPTON AREA
236 pages   117 b/w photographs   15 maps
1 870754 03 4   £16.95

Some of the very earliest ironstone quarries were located close to Northampton and the author's diligent researches have uncovered many new facts, contributing fascinating information about local history and railways. Much of the old quarrying has now disappeared under modern development, but for the benefit of industrial archaeologists, descriptions of present day remains, with grid references, are given.

PART FOUR – THE WELLINGBOROUGH AREA
240 pages   110 b/w photographs   20 maps
1 870754 04 2   £17.95

The quarries in the important Wellingborough area have been divided into four groups, based around Wellingborough, Finedon, Irthlingborough and the Nene Valley. Once again, there is much original research and many interesting historical photographs, including the last working narrow gauge ironstone line, which only ceased operation in 1966.

PART SEVEN – RUTLAND
168 pages   102 b/w photographs   11 maps
1 870754 07 7   £15.00

The ironstone quarries of Rutland obtruded very little on this quiet countryside and the few remaining scars are hidden in the folds of the hills; but the county made a significant contribution to the iron and steel industry of Scunthorpe, the North East and the Midlands and today offers a centre of efforts to preserve material relating to this now defunct industry.

PART EIGHT – SOUTH LINCOLNSHIRE
256 pages (approx)   110 b/w photographs   20 maps
1 870754 09 3   £18.95 (provisional)
Publication due in November 1990

The ironstone workings of South Lincolnshire exhibited a great variety in the way they were operated. South and west of Grantham, Great Northern Railway/ LNER mineral branches served large modern quarries at Buckminster, Colsterworth and Harlaxton, with lengthy internal railways and a great army of quarry machines. On the other hand, near Lincoln were the very old Greetwell mines dating from the 1870s, and still using horses sixty years later; while still further north were the Nettleton mines in a spectacular setting on the edge of the wolds. Between these two groups were a dozen or so small quarries in the Caythorpe area, for most of which the GNR did the quarry shunting.

The histories of these diverse systems are given in detail, including the ill-fated attempt to make Buckminster a preservation centre.

For further details of the above books and other titles in the series which are in preparation, please contact the publishers.